Cornish Cream

CORNISH CREAM

by

Phyllis Nicholson

Author of "Norney Rough"

Illustrated by
Katharine Tozer

LONDON
John Murray, Albemarle Street, W.
MCMXLII

FOR

NICK

WHO HAS HELPED SO MUCH

First Edition . . 1942

Made and Printed in Great Britain by Butler & Tanner Ltd., Frome and London

Illustrations

Contents

Chapter I

THE TOWN

CORNWALL. WHERE WAVE-WORN CLIFFS SWEEP AWAY TO AMETHYST horizons; where winds scream and sigh and shiver and little stone houses gleam in the far sunshine like forgotten pearls. Cornfields, pasture and plough, which chequer the upland in neat coloured squares, are like postage stamps of varying value, golden, green and brown.

There is wild splendour in the great Atlantic rollers, now grey, now green, now crystal-crested blue, that roll and roar and rage about the wicked black rocks, then creep, with sudden smiling calm, over the smooth silver sands.

Pollyon, in Cornwall, is no seaside place where a hemmed-in tide frets feebly against man-made piers and Council-constructed promenades. Here there never have been Bath-chairs, bands, seedy concert parties cracking threadbare jokes, moneyed mink-minded Jews, rapacious landladies or sly foreign waiters. Only fresh-faced country folk who breast the strong winds sturdily, untroubled, unmoved by seasonal changes.

There are half a dozen hotels in Pollyon, a number of guest houses and several neat streets of Apartments. The guide books tell you that the sands are superb; the bathing safe (which it is not); the golf excellent. In all that it is like many other places. But none of them say that the train comes in backwards which is unique. It's a proper train too, with a gay engine that pants and steams and sizzles, not a headless tailless electric affair with no beginning and no end like the animated worms that infest suburbia. It has windows that open and shut at will, not glassed-in tanks where half-suffocated mortals can only obtain such fresh air as the coach builders think necessary.

All the charm of Pollyon seems to be expressed by the busy little train that comes in backwards.

We are strangers here attracted by the name of " Pollyon" which looked charming on the map's Atlantic blue. A war-time holiday is something that most people do without. But the chance comes to give the children sea air. They need a change. It may be a long while before we can leave home again. Alice, best of maids, is slowly recovering from illness. She is going, rightly, to make munitions soon and may her bombs be as good as her pastry. So it is now or never. Alice will look after Nick at Norney Rough with proved devotion.

In Pollyon there is still an odd mixture of peace and war. For all its pavements, station, bank and general air of a little town it seems much further removed from world events than does Eashing Village. But Eashing is only thirty-five miles from London and that explains the subtle difference.

Sally and Sue, so small, so trusting, are happily untouched by war's alarms. Too young even to be aware of the anxiety that gnaws their elders. Here they will be in Heaven.

Cornwall is a welcoming country. It holds out its arms to strangers. Within ten days Sally and Sue have friends everywhere. The paper man, the bus conductors, the postman, all know them by name. Especially the postman. They dance round him, shouting: "Letters! Letters! Is there one from Dad?"

" Let me see . . . he's a soldier, I expect."

" He is vewy busy making holes for bombs to go in." A.R.P. in a nutshell!

The cashier of the sixpenny store asks them to Sunday tea in her home, where she plays popular tunes to them on the piano, and her brother performs on the ukulele. A sumptuous meal is provided, Cornish pasties, fried onions, fruit salad and cream. A large bunch of pinks is sent home to me.

We have no bicycles, only our own feet and Sue's little pram for transport, so we soon know every corner of Pollyon. It is not easy to get beyond it. There is neither the means nor the inducement to travel about. Our old world has gone. All memory of it is shut away in cupboards with soft pale frocks and men's flat shiny shoes.

Yet our days never lack variety. There is always something fresh to do, to see. Shops are an unending delight to Sally and Sue, fresh from village life. Here they can buy their own cakes and fruit. There is something satisfying about choosing and paying for your own supper at four years old. The branch Post Office lies beyond the pavements on a rough country road that, as yet, awaits development. Quite a different place from its big brother in the High Street, with its browny-white rubbery floor, stark shining counter and slick officials. It is full of pears, coloured post-cards, peppermint rock, and the leisurely rosy-cheeked woman in charge is easily flummoxed over postal intricacies. But she is a mine of information on how best to lay out twopence for sweets and she knows the short cut to a lovely little beach. Such knowledge is far more important than the mysteries of cabling to China.

She it was who told us to find Honeysuckle Lane. Forward to Farmer Jolly, then down into a little valley over a tiny lively stream that gleams and dimples like a roguish child. In Honeysuckle Lane honeysuckle cascades and billows all over the hedge tops that almost meet together above the green-walled pathway. What a wayward flower it is, invariably growing just out of reach. Only a few exquisite blossoms can be gathered, the rest must be left, rimming the heights with creamy stars.

The size and quality of Pollyon's shops is curiously uneven. Treloon's is staggeringly grand, with three dresses, three matching bags and hats cleverly displayed inside the big windows. The show part of the establishment is frocks and millinery, but the bigger part of the business is done at the back of the shop, where all Pollyon comes for its buttons, tape, dusters, pillow slips and towels. Not every woman in a little Cornish town wants her dress and headgear to "team up," but few can do without dish-cloths and elastic.

Treloon's, like the woman who made it, is too smart, too con-spicuous for its surroundings and does not fit in comfortably with the less ostentatious company that flanks it. Isobel's white-and-scarlet beauty salon looks awkward in the old street. But the bookshop is exactly right, with its lovely Regency windows full of sixpenny thrillers. The owner is a friendly man, but, alas, postcards and papers are the mainstay of his trade. He knows and cares nothing for books, unlike our Mr. Boutell of Godalming, who even handles a volume as if he loved it. There is no pleasure in buying from a man who is indifferent to his goods.

The girl in charge of the library hands out novels at random without even looking at the customers. Apparently her clients are in the habit of taking what is offered them.

"This is a good clean love story," she remarks, reaching for a battered book that looks neither good nor clean. The selection is not wide. I glance over them and choose one with the most full stops. The only satisfactory form of punctuation.

Here and there glaringly new buildings tower above the little fish and flower shops, small one-room affairs of great charm that shrink behind their garish brothers in the long winding street.

Gardens here are well tended, well loved. Owners, working in them at evening time, look up and smile, pleasantly, to see admiring strangers.

"You like flowers? Come in and see, we've lovely roses round the back. My husband made this greenhouse; he can't play bowls like all the men do here, can't bend, his stomach is too delicate. I do the stooping-down part of the garden, he does the stand-up jobs. Corns are my trouble. Castor oil cures them, the kind you give to dogs and cattle, ordinary sort isn't strong enough. Look at this now, I grew this rose from a cutting, five years ago; isn't it a treat? All through the winter I look forward to seeing this rose. Like one, here y'are. I've seen 'ee pass with the little children. I love children, but we never had any; my husband, Mr. Blunt, is in business. I've plenty to think about, helping him. Doesn't do to dwell on your troubles, and we've all plenty, haven't we, Doodles?" Mrs. Blunt fondles the Pekinese that takes the place of the children that did not come.

War is ever at the back of our minds, even in this distant corner where war may never penetrate during our short stay. We think of all the air protection in Surrey and look in vain for some similar precautions here.

"Have you any shelters or trenches?—with so many children coming from London there ought to be some sort of refuge for them."

"Not got one, and it's a scandal. Sleepy sorter place, Pollyon. Time it woke up. One or two of us has tried, but it's no good. Wireless tells us now we must all protect ourselves. Dad's building a shelter for us, it'll take four, us two and the babies next door. I like to hear the news at seven every morning, that kinder settles my stomick for the day, after that I don't bother. I just forget it."

The people of this little town are friendly, provided you give them time to talk. A passing "Good day" hardly establishes contact. They want to talk, endlessly, about their gardens, families, and, above all, their insides. The appendix operation that ruined their cricket season in 1936; insomnia, which dated from influenza, after the great cold of 1940; rheumatism, which can be traced to sun-bathing in damp suits.

They look fit enough, but that's not the point. Maladies are interesting to some minds, and after all somebody's sleeplessness is quite as worthy of discussion as another's golf. Many people prefer it. I for one.

A common interest in mutual ailments is one of the necessary passports to the social life of a country town. The head of the Home Guard is chosen, largely, because he is familiar with all the ins and outs of the bodies that it is his pleasure and privilege to command. In peace-time such information is of small importance, but now it is everything to know that Bob is useless for night shifts in wet weather because he's bronchial; James has hammer-toes and one flat foot. Useless for marching, but he's a tidy shot. Willy suffers from a medley of complaints, chief of which is drink. He is liable to fits if excited, so he's given a peaceful job guarding the waterworks.

And Mr. Blunt, for some unmentionable reason, cannot bend. Any person taking part in Pollyon's war effort may as well know all this.

It is such fun making people talk about themselves. Down come the shutters and we look into the most fascinating labyrinth in the world, another heart and mind, full of surprises. Sunshine lights the corners where we had thought to find cobwebs, mustiness infects the imagined fresh air.

People who want to open their hearts abound. They speak readily of their joys and sorrows. It is more interesting to hear a life story than to see the Derby. The one-legged man in charge of the bathing huts drags his roughly made wooden limb out of the deep sand with painful persistence. He wears a tiny bright ribbon when he hops along with the British Legion procession. For gallantry. His five sons are fighting. He talks of Zeebrugge in stark, vivid language, and of those after years, all pain and unemployment, or of present struggles, without bitterness. But his eyes are sad.

Who lives in all these small solid houses with gay curtains and bright gardens? "People who've made their money," says Mrs. Blunt. How did they make money in this little town that only wakes from its slow sunshiny existence for a few seasonal weeks? Until recently no one came here from the end of September until July, unless, perhaps, a solitary writer or artist seeking the solitude needful to their creative art.

Before the war Pollyon was shuttered and dust-sheeted from October until June. When summer packed up her lovely flower-strewn gowns of azure and green, and yet another harvest moon faded to nothingness before the gates of dawn, the people of Pollyon shut up their reception rooms and passed the wild winter in seclusion. No visitors came to face the terror of those wintry waves.

The crowd that blackened Cornwall's beaches in peace-time were mostly townsfolk who knew nothing and cared less for country ways. All they wanted was Cornish Cream, boy friends, daring swim-suits and dancing every night. A fickle, shifting summer crowd, like the cold-weather tourists who pass through the Far East in a day, a month, and never even catch one glimpse of her real face. She only unveils that for her true lovers.

But, apparently, the tourist trade has kept Pollyon alive—all those hot lunches on sultry August days, all those sun-blinds hiding meek double beds and rickety wardrobes—all the linoleum-plastered floors, steep stairs and poky, overworked bathrooms and little crooked attics, have produced steady incomes for their owners.

Pleasant dormouse winters are a thing of the past. Privacy has disappeared with peace. Evacuees poke their unwelcome heads in at the windows, and householders think, " Now we must work all the year round. Still, it means money. We can't afford to say ' No.' "

It is not difficult to cater for holiday crowds in care-free mood when food is cheap, abundant, and the sun, Great Yellow God, shines down from blue skies. Holiday folk are happy, prepared to be pleased with everything. But the evacuated person or family comes in quite a different frame of mind. Small wonder. It is hateful to be ejected from your own home, whether it be a slum tenement or a Georgian mansion. In time they may all come to love Cornwall. That's not the point. What does count is that they arrive in sad or truculent mood, prepared to dislike every-thing for the simple reason that no one likes having new conditions thrust upon them. Having to share a bedroom with Cousin Mary brings out the worst in most people. It's ugly to watch a woman cream her face; uglier still if she doesn't cream it. It is possible to pass the night with several persons, of both sexes, in trains, or shelters, without revulsion, but to share a bedroom with another of one's own kind is distasteful in the extreme. If there is time to think about it. Now, happily, there is not. Only the big things matter: not pinpricks, like the sight of someone else's hairs in their comb on your dressing-table.

Some of those who came to Cornwall, formerly, for a fortnight, are now here for the duration. And wisely. Not because it is safer than any other place from air attack. Raids began here almost as soon as they did anywhere. But Cornwall is cheap, gloriously healthy. No matter how long the war lasts air won't be rationed. Scores of London women with small children and fighting husbands are glad now that they have come. It's a change to live in flat shoes and tweeds, a relief to be really wanted, urgently, for some special job of local work, however small; otherwise hotel life would have driven most of these women demented after a week.

Children freed from sophisticated London clothes will grow wilder, happier, stronger. They will want to stay on and on, and their mother will think, with a catch in her heart, " When he comes home we'll live in a country cottage. He never liked London. Who kept him there? I did. What a fool I was."

Nearly every house is grey stone: innocent of paint or plaster they seem a very part of the earth herself. The police station is like a Cotswold farm, steep-roofed, and deep-set windows, the loveliest of all architectural designs, simple, perfectly balanced.

An imposing array of notices decorates the board which is not large enough to hold them all. One relating to Sheep-dipping has overflowed Rules for Enrolment in the Royal Navy, while another, dealing with Swine Fever, has become inextricably mixed with Warning of Parachute Landings. It appears that we have at last learned to refer to the Germans as Swine. Progress indeed.

This casual and chaotic presentation of orders and warnings outside Police Headquarters is quickly explained once the officers of the law appear.

The inside of a police station is new to me. Two lanky un-buttoned men answer the door.

" Good evening. Would it be possible for you to suggest that our hotel Manageress prepares some sort of air-raid shelter in the Crescent Hotel? There are many people with young children there and no precautions at all have been taken for possible fires. No sand buckets; no stirrup pumps. Could something be done?"

" We 'aven't any power about A.R.P."

No power? Strange to hear the police say they have no power! It generally oozes from their pores with obvious aggression. Policemen may be kind to old ladies at crossings, but they are a taciturn community.

" You report cases of black-out failure?"

" Yes."

" But you don't warn householders for neglecting the safety of people in their care?"

" No." Logic is not in him. He grins, slackly indifferent.

" Who is the Mayor of Pollyon?"

" There isn't one."

Ah! so that is why the town seems incomplete, like an apple tart without cloves. Perhaps it is because Pollyon is a terminus. The fact that the railway ends here, and the train, must perforce, come in backwards, perhaps affects the mentality of the natives. But Woodstock is a terminus, and Woodstock has had many lively and distinguished Mayors.

Here we have Lloyds Bank, W. H. Smith, Woolworth, the Post Office, Boots, all the props of daily life rub shoulders in the High Street. But there is no Mayor, with a comfortable beard, and wide sympathies. Mayors on their native heath command, and deserve, profound respect.

" Mr. Blunt is A.R.P. Chief. Why not go and see him?"

" Of course. I know his wife. I will."

He is the husband of the woman who loves her garden and who talks with such engaging frankness about his inside and her own problems. He is a pleasant man, who, after months of war, has just bought a booklet about incendiary bombs. His flowers are so exquisite that I forget all else. Huge mauve scabious against a granite wall, where red and white roses tumble in cascades. Lilies, the fragrant ghosts of summer nights, purple, pink and scarlet stocks and deep wine-coloured carnations flood the air with sweetness.

The small stout house faces the Atlantic that beats everlastingly upon the mighty cliffs, and creeps and crawls and curls about the little rocks and pools where small, dimpled feet go venturing. Behind, the country sweeps away, with only seagulls crying and calling above the empty fields and lanes.

" You see, we are very isolated here. I will call a meeting about these bombs in the Methodist meeting-room on Wednesday at seven-thirty."

We talk, as gardeners do, praising, apologising, picking each other's brains, and part good friends. The policemen, now buttoned up, helmeted and white-gloved, thump down the street. They salute and smile. We are all agreed.

Wednesday finds me in the Methodist meeting-room, an airy, well-kept place, booklined.

The Minister, immaculately clad, with trimly cut hair, shakes hands with all comers.

Mr. and Mrs. Blunt give me a warm welcome. What an admirable couple they are, industrious, capable, kindly. Mrs. Treloon is introduced. She looks like a London mannequin showing fashions to South American buyers. She lives in a world of grievances.

" Of course the meeting would be to-night when there's a dance for the Sailors' Wool Fund! Such a mistake having two-shilling tickets. One-and-six would have been ample."

The streak in her which has made Treloon's drapery business what it is comes out in her now with emphasis.

Fishermen in thighboots, old ladies in foulard and some active grey-haired Home Guards gather together.

The Minister is both practical and progressive. The company is neither. He checks the wordy, encourages the shy. The lecturer bristles with ideas.

During the raid ears should be plugged with cotton wool, but long twists must be left out, otherwise they will be blown inwards. (This calamity appears already to have befallen many.) Lie flat, but not quite flat. Support weight of body on elbows, to relieve jar.

If possessed of false teeth, remove same. Stick bit of rubber between teeth (or bare gums). Dummy comforters, so popular with babies, answer the purpose excellently.

How charming we shall all look, cotton wool hanging from our ears, minus teeth, plus rubber dummies.

Country folk love and understand each other. We think the same thoughts, speak the same language, fight under the same flag, acknowledging Old Mother Earth our mistress. I could talk all day to Farmer Jolly as he hoes his stony fields. No social strictures could arise to embarrass either of us. His world is full, therefore he wants no other.

But small-town business people are a different matter. New to me, and prickly as hedgehogs.

Another meeting is called for Monday ; helpers are wanted to deal with coming evacuees, so I find myself floundering in Pollyon's life-stream, lost in a thicket of social tangles.

Try as I may I can make no progress with Mrs. Treloon, the draper's wife, with her piled curls, chunky jewellery, and small, tight outlook. Healthy, happy children, a contented husband, little Noah's Arky home, proclaim her to be an admirable wife and mother. She knits for " the boys" (Army and Navy) and raises money for all manner of praiseworthy objects. Yet there is something stony and strange about her ideas, values, and personality. She is a complete enigma to me. As I am to her. There is a barrier between us stouter than the boulder wall about her glowing garden.

Procedure matters very much in the Army. It is important that the wife of a General or a Sergeant-Major be given her rightful place at any gathering. Luckily the grading system is easy. A Major's wife obviously ranks higher than the Captain's lady. There can be no argument whatever about it (unless the Captain's lady is an Earl's daughter in which case she doesn't care a hang where she sits at a dinner-party).

But who is to decide upon the relative social status of Mrs. Treloon and Mrs. Blunt? The husband of one sells drapery. The other, petrol and cars. Mrs. Blunt eats in the kitchen with the good sense which is her chief characteristic, while Mrs. Treloon is waited on in formal splendour by " the girl."

The lawyer's wife flatly refuses to know any of them and thinks " you can't be too careful." So extreme is her social caution that she can never get a fourth for bridge, which embitters her and she therefore thinks Pollyon is " absolutely lousy." On the other hand, the doctor's wife goes everywhere and is equally at home in the Vicarage or chatting to the shirt-sleeved Mr. Blunt among his cars. This makes her unpopular with some who envy her natural friendliness and easy gift of sympathetic interest.

All husbands being equal, as so many are in Pollyon, it remains for the wives to hack out some sort of status for themselves by their own effort. Mrs. Treloon, for instance, has scarlet leather chairs with steel legs in her dining-room, a daughter who can speak French, and more curls on her head than any woman in Cornwall. Further, she sleeps in a single bed, with peach draperies, alongside the " linen draper," who is no longer " bold." All very genteel, but she is often cold and lonely in her smart monogramed slumber-wear bought cheaply from the Manchester house that supplies her shop. She lies awake with her curls carefully tied up in a chiffon scarf longing for the comfortable warmth of the man who has learnt to do without her.

Here business people, kind to strangers, are awkward and difficult with each other. Mrs. Penruff, the grocer's wife, is haughty towards the tabacconist who is one of the pillars of Pollyon's activities. The grocer's shop in High Street is a glittering affair, with marble counters, glass and chromium cash desk encasing a red-haired accountant like a goldfish in a tank.

Mrs. Penruff dissociates herself from the purveying of cheese and lard and bacon by residing two miles away in Elm Avenue, and sends her children to "Ivy Lodge," select school for young ladies. They are altogether too grand for the tobacconist who trades in a side street and lives over his shop. Those who make their homes on their business premises rank in Pollyon, apparently, with the Untouchables of India.

But there are exceptions to such snobbery. Mrs. Blunt is pleasant and friendly to all comers, a capable, dignified woman, who handles First Aid Classes and the billeting of children with skill and vigour. Her garden is always at the back of her mind. She hurries home from her many good works to water the lettuces, tie up the carnations and give her flowers the love and care that all growing things need. Her out-of-doors-y outlook and manner of life make her character what it is. The sight of a boy with broken boots perturbs her no less than the sight of weeds, neglected borders, dead leaves. Her busy hands bring order, peace, contentment to all about her. She and Mrs. Treloon were girls together, but they are stiff and wary of each other in all their shared work.

" A cup of tea, Mrs. Treloon ? "

" Thank you, Mrs. Blunt."

" Sugar, Mrs. Treloon?"

" No, thank you, Mrs. Blunt."

This extreme formality is peculiar with women who meet almost daily. It may be traced to the fact that Mrs. Treloon enamels her nails (hands throughout the year, feet only in July and August, during Pollyon's " season"), and visits the hairdresser monthly; plays bridge, and ogles the lawyer. Mrs. Blunt does none of these things. She has never ogled her own husband either before or after their marriage. She leaves her hair straight; and enjoys putting manure round her roses, and washing his shirts, sure sign of being no lady in Mrs. Treloon's opinion. Their husbands play bowls and darts together with easy enjoyment, untroubled by wondering which ranks highest in the social scale, the purveying of cars, or buttons, blankets and tape.

Mrs. Blunt is like a kettle, always simmering away cheerfully, full of warmth and bubbling conversation. She thinks Mrs. Treloon superficial and supercilious, but is too busy to ponder on the shortcomings of others. Mr. Blunt owns a small garage. All have one point in common, they are Wesleyans, and Mrs. Blunt sings in the choir; like the rest of her, her voice is large, cheerful and encouraging.

There is a depth and calmness about Farmer Jolly's family who are free from the tyrannies that rule the town. Competition in their circle is wholesome and free from all pettiness, centring, as it does, in the vagaries of the land, rather than in personal peacocking or the delicate points of social status. They like to know if their potatoes are larger than the neighbouring farmer's, how much milk someone's cow gives, the cost of whitewashing the dairy sheds ; why raspberries flourish two miles away and not in their own garden. A wider, healthier view of life.

Cornwall, like Suffolk and Oxfordshire, has a character of its own, definite and interesting. These counties have never lost their personalities, never had their identity blurred and destroyed by invaders from London. Surrey, like America, is polyglot; not thoroughbred. Her few villages are as lovely as any in England, Shackleford, Eashing, Peper Harow, Seal, Cutt Mill, but beyond these few forgotten hamlets her individuality is dead. Outer London has killed it.

The old tricks of Cornish speech and manner remain.

" What's on the paper?" asks Mrs. Jolly, unfolding the local rag at day's end.

" The news is sad to-night, two trawlers lost. Italians seem a nervous lot, I've no fear o' them," says the farmer, lightly dismissing Mussolini's Army with supreme contempt. " No air raid 'ull get me mumped up in a dug-out. Cellar 'ull do fer us. It 'ud take a lot to knock these stone houses over. This farm has stud up to gales for three 'undred year; 'twould take more'n German bomb to knock it over."

Sometimes in winter they can hardly stand in the bright garden that is so quiet now. " Oft-times we goes on hands and knees round the corners autumn time," he says, sipping his tea. The cliff drops sickeningly away at the garden's edge.

Miss Blossom, kind, volcanic, sympathetic, is a typical West

Country type. She lives in the receptionist's cubby-hole of our hotel. For fifteen years she has existed under a "Do this—do that" regime, so that conversation that does not smack of orders is a rare treat to her.

She looks up, smiles, hopeful of a chat. "The little gurls 'as 'ad a happy day, Madam." Her soft Cornish voice is very pleasant. "Sleepin' fast, they are, just had a look at them, bless their hearts."

"Are you feeling better?"

"Got one of my heads to-day, tarrible bad it is, I can't hardly see." There are few days when poor Miss Blossom does not have "one of her heads."

"Look at these carnations. Aren't they luvely? For my brother's grave. I do miss him. But now 'ee's dead I do know where he is. When he was in the Army I never knew. 'Tis everything to know where our loved ones are, isn't it?"

What faith, what staggering enviable belief. Where does she get it?

"Are you a Wesleyan?"

"I am, surely." That accounts for it. "Our Minister helps us a lot, preaches luvely, he does."

The door opens to admit Mrs. False, described in the register as being "of London."

"What abaht a cupper tea?" she asks her friends. "Yes, let's."

"Tea for seven, Miss Blossom, please, in the lewange."

Mrs. False seems destined to play the rôle of childless widow. Small wonder Mr. False died. It is not Miss Blossom's work, as receptionist and booking clerk, to get bedtime tea for visitors. But the maids have gone to bed; there is no one else to do it. She rolls away, good-naturedly, to the pantry, fills the black kettle, lights the gas, lays the tray, sits down.

Mrs. False consumed bacon, toast and marmalade for breakfast. Soup, meat, two veg. and pudding for lunch. A hearty tea, followed by an ample dinner. Her only activities during the day have been talking and flicking over a newspaper. Now she wants tea.

What have our British prisoners in Germany eaten to-day?

The Food Controller said this week, "We are all soldiers in this war . . ."

Yet five spoonfuls of tea go into the pot. Tea that has been brought by British sailors over submarine-infested seas.

Miss Blossom leans forward, excitedly: "I'm leaving soon. All my life I've wanted children. Not a husband, men don't mean nothing to me, but children, yes. And now I'm going to have them. Two boys, four and six, from Hornsey. They're cummin' next Monday. Muther'll give 'em a luvely time on the farm, she'll feed 'em on chicken and cream and all, and I'll go home to 'elp her. Only a few more weeks, here," and she picks up the tray, already glimpsing the land of her dreams.

This and every hotel is full of people all wondering who the others may be. It is impossible to tell when their own setting has been wrenched away. The long-skirted person with the 1922 air looks like a village school-mistress, but she is, in reality, the Countess of X who has given up her ancestral home for a hospital. The girl who might have hailed from Hollywood is a parson's daughter, trying to get a kindergarten class together.

And who is the lumpy lady with the charmingly low voice? Passers-by glance at her, thinking "What a frightful hat! . . . etc., etc., "calamitous calves!" "Huge hips!" Or they may overlook her completely as just a dull woman who is exactly like everyone else, little dreaming that her husband may be a General, with a chest like an herbaceous border. The slick girl with six hairs above each eyebrow, who presides over Isobel's beauty shop, speaks acidly to the shapeless customer, who asks, without interest or knowledge, "for something to stop my nose from peeling."

Yet the lady who cares nothing for her appearance is a Governor's wife, and until recently rows of black servants fell flat at her approach. Half of India's Princes have lined her dining-room table; she has done valuable and far-reaching work among the Indian poor; her girlhood was spent in the shadow of Viceregal Lodge. Anyone who knows India will understand what that means.

And now she walks about Pollyon with her grandchildren, carrying home fish because the fishmonger cannot deliver to the little outlying house that she has taken.

Nobody knows that she once upheld British prestige in Bhing-Bhong, not even Mr. Pursey, the Bank Manager, who blinked at the diamonds that she deposited with him so casually. She is the type of woman who is made for export—able to endure heat, tropical storms, separation from everything she holds most dear, with smiling fortitude. A foundation stone of the Empire.

A great tide of life has swept into Pollyon bringing romance and life and movement to the little town that now rings with children's laughter. Soldiers, Infantry and Gunners. The R.A.F. and one-time cavalry that now go by on wheels. The British Army fringes our shores. British airmen police the heavens. Soldiers, both tried and untried, clatter ceaselessly up and down. Daylong, nightlong, the stainless sky is alive with planes, diving, turning, wheeling. Up they climb, in perfect formation up, up, far from sight, then down as fast as eye can follow, scattering, closing, spreading fanwise, like swallows, flying south at summer's end. Down, down, almost to the surf that rises to meet them, then up and away, sweeping the swastika from the skies. Silver dragon-flies of the welkin. Invincible.

Their day's work done, airmen come into Pollyon for such mild amusement as the town affords. They stroll along the sands, one blue arm perfunctorily clasping a girl, their hearts in heaven, for ever out of reach.

Men gather at the street corners, chewing cigarettes, looking up and down, uncertain which way to turn. Some lie on the short, sweet-smelling cliff-top turf in unbuckled disarray; others sit on the few benches. Alone, unwelcomed strangers. They have nothing to do. Nowhere to go. Girls are all very well. They fill in gaps, but that's not everything, even to war-worn troops. They want some place that is the next best thing to home. Anywhere that is not a camp.

And they shall have it.

Chapter II

THE CANTEEN

"The British Army is a mass of red-faced men with yellow moustaches!"

So wrote the pre-war schoolboy in his exercise book. It takes a war for the public to understand and appreciate soldiers. In peace-time civilians regard them as painted toys; smart, simple men with no meaning who look splendid marching about Aldershot and Knightsbridge, or who are useful at a party because they have been everywhere and seen everything. Their manners, too, are always good. There is a sort of attraction about them, both individually and as a whole. Doesn't every cook from Land's End to John o' Groat's poke her head out of the window to watch Tommy Atkins pass?

But beyond this the public knows nothing of the King's men. It is not easy to know the Army unless you belong to it. What does a man get out of it? Small pay, a meagre pension, perhaps a medal. But it gives him other things more valuable, infinitely more precious. He learns how to live and laugh and die with men. To guess their hopes, thoughts, fears. The soldier is concerned with people rather than things, therefore he has the common touch. The welfare of others is what comes first in the Army. Of how many callings can that be said?

If Private Perkins falls out on a thirty-mile route march it is for his officer to find out and remedy the cause. Why is Perkins footsore? Don't his boots fit? Are his socks too small? And if so, why? Aren't his feet as tough as those of the whole battalion? Perkins's feet, large enough at all times, assume gigantic proportions in importance.

If he were a clerk, a dock labourer, or a waiter, would his employer care very much if his toes were blistered or not? He would not even know what went on inside Perkins's boots.

There is a human touch about the Army; it makes for the good feeling and the deep comfortable happiness that springs from being well cared for. Half the vice and misery in the world would disappear if everyone felt that somebody really minded very much if their feet hurt. Why does A go out and get drunk? Because his wife forgets to ask him if his toothache is better. Why does B leave her husband for pastures new? Only because he jeers when she is tired, so tired that she can scarcely stand. Lack of sympathy can hurt cruelly.

Private Perkins hates marching for thirty miles in scorching sun or through a cutting north-easter that slices the skin from his protuberant ears. He goes on, blindly, left, right, left, right, dazed by the legs of the man in front of him that rise and fall with such maddening precision before his pain-misted eyes. But his feet are not his own affair, they belong to the Corporal, Sergeant, the Company Officers, the Regiment, the Army, almost to the Empire itself. So he must go on. He is part of a bewildering scheme that he cannot rightly understand; a tiny fragment in a vast pattern that would be incomplete without him. And that knowledge stiffens him for the last agonising mile. Somebody cares.

And now Pollyon is flooded with men like Private Perkins. They are well-fed, well-housed, well-clothed. What more do they want?

To forget that they are strangers.

Farmer Jolly fought in the last war. He knows the soldier's needs. A large tumbledown house in High Street belongs to him. Just the place for a canteen. So we attack the deserted, shuttered, cobwebbed building with broom and brush and pail, sweeping, scrubbing, dusting, while the Gas Company fit three rings in the dank mildewed kitchen. The Minister provides chairs; small tables and crockery are collected from all sources. Within a week the door is flung open. A Union Jack hung above it. One of the soldiers found it on the little pleasure ship that brought him out of Dunkirk. The soldiery swarm in, and four women struggle to serve them.

"Four eggs and tea, please."

The youthful airman with 'Joined Yesterday' written all over him gives his order with a charming smile. Alas! there are no eggs. There was no canteen until an hour ago. Only the barest necessities have as yet been unpacked.

"Sausage roll and tea, please."

Thank Heaven we've got both.

"How much the ham sandwiches?"

"Can we write letters here?"

"May we have a wash?"

"Any cigarettes?"

The steady stream of nailed boots pours in. The tiny kitchen is piled with stores. We cut and cut and cut at the big sweet-smelling Cornish loaves. Voices from London, Scotland, Ireland and all the English counties echo across these blue and white table covers, where bunches of summer flowers and the smell of fresh tea mingle in homely welcome.

One big room is set apart for refreshments. Long windows overlook the harbour. A counter is improvised at one end, made from barrack tables, covered with gay oilcloth, where cakes, sandwiches, soft drinks are displayed and the tea is poured out.

Here sits the Duchess, moving spirit of the canteen. The name suits her exactly; everyone calls her that. Her home is a great grey house, beyond Pollyon. She lives in two rooms of it. The rest is filled with people who haven't any homes.

Generations of culture, grace and dignity have given her a beauty that never grows old.

Calm, stately, efficient, she touches the teapot with slender, sensitive fingers, testing its warmth mechanically, but her mind is far away. In the last war she was young, handsome, avid for experience, and she had grasped it with both hands. So had he. She nursed him, washed his wounds, made his bed. Then he was killed, and she went back to the great stone house of her ancestors, with peacocks on the terrace, and cedars on the lawn. She tried to find forgetfulness in a thousand ways, and, now, once more soldiers are surging about her. The same leathery faces, the same jokes, the same swift comings and goings. Everything much the same as it had been long, long ago. But she was different.

Behind the counter is a hatch into the little kitchen, through which all the food and crockery is passed. The scullery lies beyond, and there the washing-up is done. So far there is no table, only chairs on which to stack the great piles of used plates and cups.

But we can feed the men. That is what matters. Their voices drift through the hatch.

"There's wun thing No German 'ull ever face, and that's a British bayonet." Spike, the Ploughshire Infantryman, is speaking.

"That's richt, lad. A Breetish bayonet, with a Scotsman behind it, that makes 'em rhun."

"German's infantry's no good."

"Ah wud not say thaat."

"Perhaps you fellars from London didn't stay to see any."

Gusts of laughter follow, teeth and eyeballs gleam whitely in tanned faces. The room is full of smoke and laughter and the everlasting tramp of black Army boots.

Here are the men who have defeated Germany. Privates, Lance-Corporals, Sergeants. Regulars or militiamen, it's all the same. Ploughmen, boys from our shameful slums, who never had a square meal until the Army fed them. Hitler knew, none better, that they are unbeatable. Traitor-ridden France, rotted from within, and little trampled countries gave him momentary triumphs, but he flinches to face the British.

It's not the Generals who win our wars, but the quality of our men. The finest strategy in the world is useless without solid backing. The British Army, Navy, Air Force do not depend upon a few star turns to stage successful battles. The seeds of victory are in the hearts and bodies and spirits of these ordinary soldiers. Their leaders know it. The Germans know it. All the world knows it.

The huge red-haired gunner from Glasgow, apparently called Ginger Scot, harangues the company.

"We deed our best, but we hadna got the guns. If we had had sufficient guns and tanks, not a Gairman in sight would ha' been alive noo."

He lumbers forward. "Two ma pasties, please, it's verra nice to have them hot."

Spike, tough, indomitable, calm as the county that bred him says to Ginger, "A bayonet's good enough for me. We 'ad plenty of 'em; we've got 'em still. You can only use a shell once. Bayonets last."

His belief in bayonets has earned him the name of Spike.

He puts a whole doughnut into his mouth, bringing conversation to a close. At intervals he asks:

"Doughnut, please." He eats five.

"Do they feed you well in camp?" asks one of the helpers.

"No, mam."

"Do you get enough?"

"No, mam."

"Is it well cooked?"

"No, mam. Cornish pasty, please."

"Hot?"

"Kin you make it 'ot?"

"Certainly."

"Thank you, 'ot, then."

"Knife and fork, please."

A curious request, not made before. Even the most elegant airmen are eating them in their fingers.

We search about, find him some tinny cutlery of shining newness. He takes them clumsily, drops the fork, then abandons it and halves the pasty with his strong teeth. Strolling about, glancing at the papers, he parks the pasty on the mantelpiece, across the window ledge and finally vanishes with it upstairs.

He soon comes back.

"Kin I buy a stamp, please? For a letter, 'ow much is that?" Brown hands fumble clumsily at his pocket.

" I've got one, do take it."

" Thank you, how much?"

Sixpence is extended, finally withdrawn, the gift accepted, with a slow smile. " Kin I write in that corner?"

" There's a writing-room upstairs."

" This'll do fine."

With the utmost deliberation he removes his cap, loosens his collar, takes up the pen, examines it, on second thoughts lays it down. Fortifies himself with tea. Selects a sheet of paper, then with elbows spread and awkwardly sprawling feet the letter is begun.

Who will receive it? Wife, mother, girl? Has she any idea how long he takes to pen those lines? What does he think, and say? Is he homesick, lonely? The envelope is addressed. Now for the stamp. Where is it? Spike scrutinises the table, floor, his knees. Not there.

" Dropped something?" shrills somebody from the counter.

" Yes, mam. Stamp." By this time he is on all fours.

" There! It's stuck underneath your boot."

At last letter, envelope and stamp are all assembled. Spike heaves a sigh of relief, comes forward, cup in hand.

" Another tea, please, mam," adding naïvely, " I've wrote my letter."

Every type of British manhood comes here for refreshment. Labourers from docks and fields, clerks, shopmen, sons of Brigadiers and bus drivers, old soldiers and new in all their infinite variety unified, outwardly, by war. Miles of Air Force blue and khaki cloth may make a thousand men appear alike, but the personality of every one remains unique, individual. When soldiers muster on parade they all look just the same, their uniformity is almost maddening. They work and move as one. Their bodies may be marshalled into squares and columns, but their minds, never. Unlike our enemies, who cannot think nor act except in masses, linked together as buttons on a card they look impressive enough collectively, but snap the string that holds them and they scatter, uselessly.

The Air Force is an aloof body, far too polite to be called standoffish. They would never think it smart to be rude, as some of the cavalry regiments did in the dark ages between two wars.

But they are more buttoned up than soldiers. They share cigarettes, newspapers and the set-out sugar ration with the B.E.F., but there is no fraternising between them. Khaki and blue are never seen sitting or walking together.

There is a subtle difference in their way of greeting and farewell. The fliers, say, on arrival, "Hullo," "Good day" or merely "Tea, please." A few even, "How de do." And when they leave, it is "Toodle-oo," "Night-night," "Bye-bye."

I can't imagine Ginger Scot or Spike saying "Toodle-oo" to any of us. The old, regular, pre-war soldier is unmistakable, in looks and manner to those who have known and loved him always. Britain's greatest ambassadors. The men behind the Crown. Spike is a regular. His family have served in the same regiment for generations. As boys they follow the plough; when the Army needs them no more, they go back to the plough. There is nothing slick or smart about Spike. He is clean, simple, well-mannered, utterly content. Not large, not small, his determined body has faced, and survived, all the foulest horrors of war. Has he ever been afraid? One knows, instinctively, that he would shrink from nothing. There is comfort even in being near him. His bright blue eyes are almost childlike in his square red face.

"It's nice to come in 'ere, kinder homely."

"I'd send every woman and child ter Canada," broadcasts Alf, who talks without breathing in tones that penetrate all barriers. "Leave us be'ind to settle the Germans, we'd do that right enough."

"And what would they do in Canada?"

"Work, same as they do 'ere. Nice change for 'em."

"I wouldna hae my wife and family sent to abroad," says Ginger Scot fiercely. "Think of the submarines, man. They are happier at hoam, even if it is not safe any longer. Safety is not everything to them hoam is. War-time's bad enough for women anyway without sending them to a strange country."

Alf bridles. "Maybe yer live on a Scotch moor with no heowses near. Ever bin to London?"

Ginger nods. He marched across it once, from Victoria to Paddington.

"Not margarine on *both* sides of the bread, ham is very expensive." Mrs. Treloon's cold voice is at my elbow. Loaves and margarine, waiting to be converted into palatable sandwiches, surround us.

"But we can't charge twopence for a sandwich and only butter half of it."

" Ham is very difficult to get."

" The men pay for what they have.   Good value must be given. Should we pay twopence for a railway station sandwich that was only margarined on one side?   No."

" We must not forget that this is war-time."

The corrugated head covers a mean mind.

" More ham sandwiches, please," calls the Duchess, through the hatch, " they are going fast; the men like them, and a plate of sardine ones too.   Six packets cigarettes, from the store cupboard."

Eight.   Nine.   Ten.   The squares are cut, mustarded, the limp pink ham, white-edged with fat, is fitted to the bread, liberally; sardines, egg and tomato is quickly mashed, more slices spread. The kettle boils over: piled cups and plates are pushed through to be washed.

" More sugar, please."

" Fresh tea, please."

Lighter steps in the stone passage.   Not nailed.   Airmen.   We can tell by their feet.   That means poached eggs.   Mr. Jolly has just brought some in.   A swift search about the meagre scullery reveals nothing but a small saucepan.

" Is there an egg poacher here?"

" Should be.   Mrs. Blunt promised to bring one."

" She's meeting evacuees, six hundred come to-day."

" Never mind, I'll manage."

The small capable woman, who looks so tired, cracks the fat Cornish eggs expertly and, though she lacks everything in the way of tools, she miraculously produces fluffy white blobs unsullied by streaky yolks, on squares of toast.   Hot plates, fresh tea are pushed through to the counter.   Conversation slackens as the men eat.

Summer sunlight pours into the kitchen across the old stained walls, tattered linoleum and rusty, disused grate.   It warms the drab scullery sink and battered taps, finds a reflection in the bright gas rings, installed but yesterday, in crude contrast to such dilapidated surroundings.

" Seems a bit of a lull now, let's 'ave a cupper tea."

The little woman with the tired face and swollen ankles drops on to a kitchen chair.

" Plenty to do here. Good thing. Helps one to forget." She pours out my tea, sips her own, reflectively.

A start, at any rate, has been made.

After a few days the canteen is in running order. Stores are all neatly shelved; a regular roster of helpers made out and hung up for all to see. Four workers to every four-hour shift. One behind the counter to pour tea, take orders, check the cash, three in kitchen and scullery to share the preparation of food and general cleaning. An extra one for Fridays and Saturdays, the busiest times.

When the Duchess is on the afternoon shift I am given charge of the buffet, and, alas, the cash-box for the evening. But it's a welcome change from sandwich cutting in the kitchen. The " cash-box" is a pie dish filled with pence and a few pieces of silver. A penny account book and a pointless pencil lie beside it. Spike advances, asks for the usual coupla doughnuts and tea. Threepence. That's easy. An airman wants three sausage rolls, lemonade, slice of currant cake, packet of cigarettes. He proffers ten shillings. I count the change on my fingers and welcome his " Quite right." Steps thicken across the threshold, tables fill to capacity, the overflow sit up the stairs or carry their plates and cups to the writing-room. Many stand.

A flood of khaki and blue surges about us. Cornish pasty for the gunner sergeant; weak tea, no sugar for the sandy-haired private; ginger beer and sandwiches for the boy with a bandaged hand; cigarettes for the man with a new medal ribbon. 6d. 7d., 8d., 9½d., how much is that from 2s. 6d.? Oh, to have had a higher education!

" Can anyone change ten shillings please?" 4d. to come out of it, 9s. 8d.—why is that so much easier than 9½d. from 2s. 6d.?

" Cigarettes? Sold out, so sorry." There is no one to send for more. Miss Jolly is buried behind dirty crockery, and the sandwich cutter works feverishly with aching hands.

" I'll go," somebody volunteers.

" Thank you, here's ten shillings."

Heavens! He has gone, what did he look like, blue eyes? One

stripe? Can't remember, will he ever come back? Never, never shall Mrs. Treloon find out that I cannot add up.

How often in my ignorance have I waited, impatiently, at Waterloo Station for a cup of tea and Bath bun. How slow the waitresses always seemed. Now I realise that her arms and feet and head all ached at the same time and half of her was worrying over the small child at home with measles, while the other half was thinking, frantically, "Bath bun for woman in black, ham sandwich and beer for gent in brown trilby."

The setting and removal of food and crockery on small tables overhung with heads, draped with elbows and bristling with thrust-out legs is not always easy. A burly sergeant with spreadeagled arms suddenly throws back his head with a cheery guffaw at the precise moment that his tea is set before him. Hot liquid slops in all directions. A tiny handkerchief, of the "show" rather than the "blow" type is rubbed over his splashed shoulders. Some-one grovels for the spoon. Grains of sugar, precious as gold dust, are trampled underfoot. A cloth is fetched. The table duly wiped, while waiting customers queue up with incredible speed.

Then at the end of the shift, accounts must be squared and handed over to the newcomer. Minerals, so much. Teas, so much. Cigarettes, how much? It won't come right. Nothing will make it. Not even the sly slipping in of pence from private sources. All the fine, well-filled bodies in the room are full of buns and tea and pasties. How many cakes are inside the sergeant-major, four or six? I can't remember, nor does he. Smoke thickens, cups clatter, customers stream in, and the "cash-box" overflows with silver and coppers. But nothing balances.

"Ah, take the cash in hand and waive the rest . . ." But Mrs. Treloon cannot be waived. A man with white teeth and amused eyes picks up the pencil and the blue plate and the penny book.

"How much did you start with?"

"No idea. Never counted."

"That's a pity." He puts it all straight, laughs and goes out whistling, just as our reliefs come in to take over.

A kitchen outlook is quickly acquired in canteen work. Is the sink clean? Did the last shift wash all the teacloths and hang them in the air to dry and sweeten? Are the tea-leaves always consigned to the bucket provided to receive them, or do some helpers throw them down the drain?

We know now exactly what trials and tribulations maids have to endure. It is one thing to work in your own kitchen for your own family, quite another to live in someone else's where grubby walls, broken floorboards and frowsty cupboards have to be endured because the correction of these shortcomings lies in other hands. So many minor difficulties and discomforts hamper and hinder jobs that could otherwise be efficiently carried out.

There is not nearly enough crockery, which means that time given to washing up must be stolen from sandwich cutting. Then the men have to wait, which is unfortunate. Prompt service fosters good feeling. There are many helpers, but the slowness of some is intolerable. We should get on far better without them. The Duchess runs a long finger down the list of names murmuring, " So-and-so must go, but it's not easy. She paid for all the black-out curtains and provided a wireless." Surely having already played her part she can be tactfully placed on the retired list.

And what a wireless it is! All spits and shrieks and groans. Half a dozen words of the news, a sudden gust of music, a detached meaningless laugh, sometimes comes through. No more. It is worse than nothing since the sight of it raises hopes doomed to be dashed.

So the Duchess brings her parrot into the canteen. She thinks it may amuse the men. It does. Daisy, so called since she never gives an answer, detests all women. No female except her mistress can touch her. Should one approach she lowers her head, fluffs out her feathers and becomes a veritable German eagle spitting hate.

But when the smallest, silliest man approaches, her demeanour changes instantly. She sidles up and down on turned-in toes, crooning with delight and inviting advances. Should he be bold enough to extend a finger she will caress it gently with her cruel beak, opening and shutting her beady eyes in paroxysms of emotion.

She is never the same for two days together and is always full of surprises, her wholly unaccountable behaviour being one of her few charms. She will sulk for hours, then, for no reason whatever will whistle " Rule Britannia" with real feeling. When asked " Want some sugar?" she replies " Good morning." After hours of tuition over some new phrase, during which she maintains complete silence, she will unexpectedly yell, " Pay-day to-day!" instead of " Hullo, everybody!" which is her daily lesson.

She loves Spike. His rough hands, that can be so gentle, have helped animals in and out of life on his father's farm for many years. There is complete understanding between him and them; a rare sympathy that is inbred and which can never be cultivated. He stands staring at Daisy, scratching her neck with his clean red finger, while she preens and arches herself with pleasurable croonings. He tries, with the slow, endless patience of his kind, to make her say, " Tea, please." She listens with acute attention and sits so still that her lovely pink and pearly grey plumage might be made of painted plush.

But no word comes. She only stares unblinkingly. " You'll get it one day," says Spike, philosophically, as he turns away.

Mrs. Blunt and Miss Jolly are booked for Friday and Saturday nights. Pity they can't come oftener, as both they and the curly Mrs. Treloon are models of industry and method. But they are only three out of two dozen. More than half are wasteful and unthinking, slopping ham on to the middle of the bread leaving the edges without meat or margarine. This not only makes a dull sandwich but it means that ends are left on the plates. Prices are low enough. Every crumb should be made palatable for the shallow-pursed soldiers.

The bread-cutting machine, long and eagerly awaited, is not a success. It cuts many fingers but few loaves. The wicked steel hoop with razor-like edge merely reduces the loaf to unusable tatters. Old bread, new bread, middle-aged bread, it is all the same, so we slice with carving knives instead, and leave the guillotine alone with " Mind your fingers" stuck into the table beside it.

In spite of inevitable small differences and misunderstandings a real thread of friendliness and good cheer runs through the organisation of the establishment. All are ready to help each other (except over the Gent's Cloak). There is no rush to clean this apartment. Helpers enjoy standing behind the counter chatting to the men, which is natural enough. But the grimy wash-basins, broken fragments of soap and stale towels are a reproach to the Union Jack which flutters from the doorway.

" Where is the disinfectant?"

" Sorry, there is none."

" Never mind. May I buy some myself?"

" The cash is locked up. Mrs. Treloon has not yet come."

" I'll pay myself."

" But that would complicate the accounts."

How can it? A bottle can't masquerade in cash columns as
1s. 6d. The canteen is so poor that even the smallest gift can
surely be accepted?

Miss Jolly lifts up the fat kettle, which is labelled " Please keep
full and boiling," half fills a bucket, gathers up cloths and brushes.
We creep furtively upstairs, leaving the huge kettle full but not
quite boiling. The Air Force must wait five minutes for their
tea if the Toilet is to be cleaned.

Cigarette ends and cherry-stones lie thickly embedded on the
landing floor. We sweep first, then scrub with the strong germ-
killer that smells pleasantly of lemons and carbolic. Fly-blown
windows are flung open, cleaned. Soon taps and porcelain surfaces begin to brighten. New soap and rough gaily striped towels
from the sixpenny store embellish the basins that now shine instead
of sulk. Just in time as Spike ambles up the stairs.

" Looks a lot better now." He hangs in the writing-room
doorway, trying to say something.

" Got me forty-eight hours' leave, going home to Woodstock."
How welcome is the sound of his broad, deep voice. " It's a
powerful long way." Woodstock, the lovely little grey stone
town, with wide fields sweeping gently away from it and elms
dappling the hollows with their plumy heads.

" But I only gits outer the train twice. First at London, Paddington they calls that; then you go to another platform and arsts
fur Oxford. A bus goes from there."

" Yes, I know."

So he comes from Oxfordshire too—then we are " fellow clay."

He goes out and a man-eater walks in. She sits down in the
canteen, crosses her legs and remarks brightly, " I'd like to work
here." Her beach wrap falls away, leaving highly developed legs
bare to the uttermost thigh limit. Arms, neck, legs, everything
about her is bare; especially her face. Thank goodness the Duchess
is on duty. She can deal with anything from drunks downward
—or upward.

But the girl is not easily put off. " I hear you are short-handed. I want to do some war work."

There is no one in the canteen but Spike and an Air Force sergeant. Daisy, the parrot, spits hate at the intruding female; perhaps she sees in her a possible rival to Spike's affections. Spike does not even look up, he goes on repeating " Tea, please, tea, please," to his feathered friend and the airman reads on. The girl's eyes rake the room, noting a " common little private" and the man who does not look at her, but an R.A.F. sergeant is well worth trying for. She realises that she made a mistake coming here half-naked.

" Hell," she thinks, " ought to have worn a frock, and even stockings; always making mistakes and this tall woman was going to be difficult, she'd never met anyone like her before." To her surprise the answer was favourable; not in the least what she had expected.

" Of course. Exactly. Friday night, our busiest time, thank you very much."

So the following Friday the unbuttoned lady arrives and the Duchess directs her to the scullery sink. She is kept standing there for four hours. At eight o'clock she asks to go, suddenly remembering a cinema appointment. The Duchess points out, charmingly, that each shift finishes the work they undertake, and that the night helpers sweep and tidy back premises before leaving.

It was the girl's first and last visit.

Gradually we all warm to our work; and come to know each other. Many worlds meet and mingle here. At first Mrs. Treloon is astonished to see Spike nervously offering the Duchess a Woodbine, in part payment of many that she has given him. She is amazed to hear a charming voice say " Thanks very much, just right for a short smoke, aren't they?" But new ways soon become old ones.

Mrs. Treloon is a marvellous business woman; a clever cook, an efficient housekeeper. That we all have much to learn from her is obvious and yet what an obstructionist she can be.

The men crowd against the counter, their few pence in their hands.

" Pasties, please."

" Hot pasties."

"Hot Cornish pasties."

It seems so little to ask. They have walked for miles. Their pay is small. No other place in Pollyon caters for their simple needs.

"We can't heat the pasties any more. Gas is too expensive."

"Who pays for it?" asks the Duchess, in no way flattened by her Woodbine.

"It's very expensive."

That is no answer. Businesses may be built up by the avoidance of questions, but Spike shall have hot pasties if we swing for it.

"This is Dad's house," whispers Miss Jolly, as the curled, calculating head is withdrawn from the hatch. "He's glad to let the men have it. If there's no rent we can afford gas out of the takings. We'll ask him when this shift's over."

Mr. Jolly, who is both farmer and Finance Minister, lives over the hill. His daughter swills out the hundred-and-fiftieth cup, I dry it, wash out the wet cloths, peg them on the line. We sweep the scullery floor, scrub the sink.

"Back way's shortest." We scramble up a pebbly path towards a stone farmhouse. Hydrangea clumps billow about the gates, ghostly pale in the evening light, and a group of palms stretch their giant leaves against a celadon sky laced with scarlet. The smell of honeysuckle is hauntingly sweet. It will be blooming now at Norney Rough, round the nursery windows where childish laughter has, momentarily, died. Are the roses blossoming about the clothes-line that is generally alive with tiny garments dancing in the wind? Where is Nick? What is he doing? Eating his supper of strong tea and sardines from a clothless table in the Control, and writing a book in the lulls between raid warnings. It does not bother him to do several things at once.

Mr. Jolly, short, kindly, with sailor-blue eyes, is bringing in the cows. Not a man to grudge a penn'orth of gas.

"Will 'ee come in and have a bit of supper?" The meal is laid. White china on a blue cloth. A great black kettle bubbles on the fire. Bits of bright brass gleam about the walls. The floor is stone, mighty flags grooved with the passing feet of years. Mrs. Jolly is broad and welcoming.

We eat scrambled eggs, coarse brown bread, gooseberry tart and clotted cream, followed by tea in large, thick cups.

"I like something hot, after the day's work," says Farmer Jolly. So does Spike. "Heat the pasties? Of course, heat 'em. No need to stint the gas."

Miss Jolly looks at me; smiles. How happy this agricultural atmosphere is.

"There's two or three fresh eggs for the canteen, will you take them on your way back?"

Yes, indeed, I pass the door. Farewells are made, an invitation to come again given, and gladly accepted. The sun has gone behind the little town's grey roof. It is almost dark. The canteen is emptying as I take in the eggs. The last blue coat turns campwards. The last nailed boot rings over the threshold. Lights out.

Chapter III

THE HOTEL

Two soldiers are in the hall. One thin. One fat. They have papers in their hands. That means the hotel is to be commandeered. I approach with diffidence.

"Is the hotel to be taken over by the Government?"

"Probably, to-morrow," is the crisp, uncaring answer. Then, thawing at the sight of Sally and Sue:

"You staying here?"

"Yes."

"Then you will be wise to move into rooms; some smaller place than this where you won't be turned out; right in the country."

"We are not evacuees."

The toy train would take us home to-morrow, but it would be a pity to leave when Pollyon has taken us to her heart.

What is the alternative? A remote Cornish farm? Not good enough. One of the children might break an ankle; there would be no 'phone, no bus, no car by which to summon immediate aid.

The men nod casually:

" We'll be along later."

I'll find rooms in Pollyon. Quickly, before all are full. The hotel management recommend Fernbank, a neat house with rose-massed garden. An angular woman opens the door. Here, obviously, is the proverbial thorn.

" Two bedrooms? Yes, free now. A little sitting-room too."

" Oh! children! I didn't know you had children. We generally take elderly couples. Mother doesn't like noise."

Sue's curled-framed eyes look up at the lined, spectacled face above her. The woman turns away, only to be greeted by Sally's frank smile on the other side.

" Well . . . would you like to see the rooms?" The question comes reluctantly. We are obviously not wanted.

So this is how wandering musicians, tramps, evacuated wives, girls who go wrong, feel standing about on other people's door-steps, being scrutinised by hostile eyes. It is an odd sensation to be bereft of background, to wait before a strange door asking for a bed. We grow used to our own setting and the solid serenity that goes with it. The soldier's wife has the regiment; the parson's lady her parish; business women their commercial colleagues. But the evacuated wife has nothing and nobody. Not until we have, ourselves, stood upon an unknown threshold, asking unsym-pathetic strangers for a bed, can we appreciate her dilemma. The frame of her existence has been wrenched away. Only her own personality is left.

Shopkeepers will give her scant attention because she is not an important personage. No one will ask if she is warm or cold or comfortable because they want invitations to her delightful parties. She is taken entirely upon her merits. Perhaps in time the green-grocer will pick her out the ripest fruit because he really likes her.

Here are the rooms. Two. Large. Airy. Linoleum on the floor. Texts on the walls. Double brass-balled beds with thick white cotton coverlets, edged with a looped fringe of intricate Victorian design. An air of chilly cleanliness pervades both landlady and apartments.

Does her heart really beat? Has anyone ever flung their arms round those frigid shoulders? Is her blood red? She assures us " that half Devonshire is sleeping on the floor." Yes, yes, of course, we are very lucky to get in. Money is mentioned. Agreed upon. We can come in three days. Inestimable privilege!

But Army orders are not new to me. Whitehall, like woman, says one thing, does another. We are not yet ejected from the Crescent Hotel.

Forlorn groups gather in the hall discussing the immediate future. Little Mr. Friske is broadcasting excellent advice to a group of frightened families. "I've known Pollyon for thirty years. Don't go into rooms, or take a bungalow. It works out more expensive. Stay in a hotel on a flat rate. Then you know where you are."

"But the military said . . ."

"There's more'n one hotel in Pollyon. The military won't take them all."

Next morning Miss Blossom, usually so active, hangs about the doorway doing nothing.

"The military said they'd be here at nine. It's ten already. I can't understand it."

She is waiting to be relieved by the British forces, like a beleaguered garrison. Now and then she steps outside, scans the street, even the sky, expecting perhaps a message by air.

"They may not come, Miss Blossom."

"But they said they would." Poor trusting creature. She waited until lunch-time. All the afternoon, and the next day. Still no news. After two days of tense expectation the flutter in the hotel dovecote dies down. Another British crisis has passed.

The buff files holding the particulars of Pollyon lie forgotten on the back seat of an Army car in a London garage while the military are amusing themselves with ladies.

The Crescent Hotel is a rambling old house with comfortable bow windows and fat chimneys. Its cream-washed face looks fresh and welcoming behind the short gravelled drive flanked by hydrangeas. The entrances are labelled "IN" and "OUT" with neat precision, but the vestibule is depressing. Turkey carpet. Brown paint. Brass tables and old ladies everywhere peering suspiciously at all who come and go. Their drab frocks, colourless faces and general air of depression cast a chill over the newcomer. When shops are full of glorious colours; hairdressers and wig-makers abound; while creams and powders are still obtainable, why say no to them all? Miss Blossom doesn't. She opens her arms wide to catch the full glory of life. Neither youth nor beauty is hers, but she has vitality and vigour to balance their loss. She manages her clothes so well that her figure seems to be merely comfortably plump rather than overblown, and if her hair is "helped" to such surpassing goldness it does but match the colour of her heart. She sits in a small glazed pen under the stairs; without her the Crescent would have fallen to pieces long ago. Madam, the proprietress, is a childless widow. A watery personality dimmed by grief.

"Ah! when Master was here," says Miss Blossom, regretfully, "everything was slick and proper then. Run this place like a battleship, he did. People—food—money—he understood them all."

Which Madam does not. She is timid where boldness is required; awkward where adroitness might win the day. She clings, pathetically, to her home, bewildered, saddened, irritated at the rising tide of confusion which she is unable to stem. All beauty and brightness died for her with the robust man to whom obstacles were merely opportunities. She longs for the ordered peace and comfort that grew with such apparent ease under his skilful hands and tries to smother the greyness in her heart by wearing vivid greens and harsh blues. He loved colour.

Miss Blossom's deep voice is warm and welcoming. Her ready smile lights upon the children with genuine interest. She ought to have complete control of the staff because she understands her fellow-men, and her standards are high. Everyone works better for someone who expects a lot. It increases their self-respect. Domestic difficulties are doubled by war conditions. The very few maids who are left only go, naturally, to the best places.

Who will put up with lumpy beds and dull food when the best of both are to be had for the asking? And it is depressing to be caught in the web of disorder that is born of a muddled mentality.

One day 'The Cliffs' head-waiter strolls in, a grand gentleman from the huge hotel five miles away.

"We've been commandeered," he announces; "the military take over next week. It's only the big places they want."

His glance shrivels the Crescent lounge, tries to shrivel Miss Blossom, and fails entirely to do so.

" Then you'll be out of a job," she smiles pleasantly. " We could do with a good waiter, ours is flat-footed and that rude."

Nobody pays eight guineas weekly for a bedroom at ' The Cliffs' now. Perhaps they never will again. Soldiers sleep in rows upon the floor where, formerly, livery old ladies snoozed in splendid isolation. Strawberries and cream, duck and green peas, soufflés light as air, fine old wines and fragrant coffee are no more served in the long-mirrored dining-room. Barrack tables, lined with rows of leathery faces, now stand on the bare boards; nailed boots clatter about the empty echoing hall once filled with leisured, golf-playing company directors. The stairs, so richly carpeted before, are naked now. An orderly scrubs them once a week with yellow soap; and under the great chandelier, brought from Venice years ago by the oily Italian manager, young soldiers gather, learning the hideous business of war.

Our hotel terms are moderate enough. There are no extra charges. We are teetotallers and inhabit back rooms. No friends come for meals. My entertaining expenses are limited, so far, to penny cups of tea periodically, to the canteen helpers. And yet the weekly total is a staggering one. If we lived here for a year, as many unfortunate evacuees have done, our Budget, like that of the Italians, would amount to something like two million deficit. But when figures assume those proportions all concerned are past caring.

True, the food is excellent. Meals more substantial than in our own home, but it is strange that so simple a life should be costly. Two little bedrooms with no fireplaces don't look expensive. But they are.

We are not used to hiring rooms or houses. We have once paid rent to a millionaire Indian landlord, who smilingly invited us to inspect his large boxes full of jewels, but refused to spend a few rupees in whitewashing the drawing-room. An odious situation which determined us to buy our eventual abode.

The hire of hotel rooms seems high at all times, but no doubt wear and tear must be paid for. Some patrons probably leave cigar ends in their beds, drop ink on the carpets or come in drunk, which must cause the proprietor mental and financial racket. So sober folk like ourselves must pay for the black sheep, in the way that for one man who pays his tailor three do not.

It's everything to own a home in war even though His Majesty's Government may see fit to fill it with loud-booted soldiery. Norney Rough is ours, every brick and tree of it. There is no threatening landlord to turn us out, no bullying owner to intimidate us with important papers about leases written in print the size of sand grains. If the Government want your home they take it. There is no argument. You go out. They come in. There it ends. I know, having lived in many Government quarters.

"House property is the most valuable asset to-day," states Mr. Friske, man of boundless energy and ability. "Especially in the country. I own houses in London, many more in Margate. All empty, dead loss now, but the land is mine and the sites are good. If all my houses are bombed the land remains. That can't be destroyed." Unlike Mrs. Treloon, who puts her trust in chariots and spends her all upon silks and furs and perms which even one small incendiary could well wreck for ever.

Our vegetable garden, wooed and won at last, is producing crop after crop with praiseworthy steadiness. Not only do Nick and Alice feast upon succulent peas and fat tomatoes warmed by sunshine, but he can now take regular basketfuls of home-grown produce to town friends who must otherwise buy. Even in midwinter the supply is adequate with perennial spinach, beetroot, artichokes. Baskets of potatoes are given a warm reception by mothers who have little Londoners to cater for in addition to their own family.

Here, Madam has troubles galore. That is evident. Chef is a clever cook, but not an adaptable one. He was brought up on the "take a dozen eggs" system. Food is his joy, the light of his eyes. To him, the sight of foamy omelettes, flagons of cream, huge hams, fat pheasants, iced cakes, oysters, great glistening salmon, is a passport to Paradise. He was born for peace. Not war. And now that he must perforce make meals out of bits and ends, the iron has entered into his soul. He adores the children, who love to watch him decorating the milk jellies that he makes for their supper. He airs his grievances to me in the kitchen, while Sue perches on the table, scraping jam from a saucer.

"I am not staying here," he would say to me. "Look where I have to sleep! Out there! Next the pantry. Not even decent bedclothes. Old rugs and a wretched mattress." He slept there, happily, before rationing was introduced, apparently.

"Look at the maids' quarters!" I had. Sue had followed the housemaid up one day and I found the dreariest room with drab paper looking on to a brick wall three feet outside the window. Beds were packed into it all anyhow. The few chairs and tables were battered, broken. Everything there ought to have been thrown into the sea. In Master's time it had been a box-room. He believed in making everybody comfortable. If it had to become a bedroom, couldn't the walls have been distempered pale yellow, furniture and beds coloured to match? Why didn't two or three girls sleep here instead of six? Why wasn't another window made on the far side of the room, where no outer wall impeded ventilation? Madam starts her business at the wrong end. Her foundations are set upon the sand. She begins with the visitors instead of starting with the staff.

Does it never occur to her that the maids can't get adequate sleep because of headaches caused by lack of fresh air? But every tiny dressing-room must be kept free for the " Season" which, happily for us, no longer exists. Those hectic peace-time summer weeks. Cornwall is having a war season of another sort.

But in spite of its haphazard organisation, dusty corners and Nothing To Do Patrons, we are very happy in the Crescent. There is a certain charm about my tiny room with the creaking boards and the maddening cupboard that will not shut. The curtains all fall down when sharply pulled back and the foot wide gap between their edges has to be filled, nightly, with a black paper blind of contradictory habits. But walls and carpet are a soft green, the kind of horizon green that comes with twilight. The paint yellowy white, like Cornish cream. There is a fixed wash-basin and the bed is excellent. Outside the one wide window little houses and gardens melt into the farms and fields beyond. The white-plumed toy train ambles across the landscape. Our link with Nick.

Bed-sitting-room life has much to recommend it. Endless exertion is saved. Three steps to the dressing-table; four to the typewriter; one leap into bed. And the children's room opens into mine. Their activities can thus be heard and supervised without moving. A supreme advantage.

There is no room for hoarding even of the mildest nature. Where can these six writing-pads, three packets of paper handkerchiefs and balls of wool for winter jerseys go? A box under the bed is the only possible solution, a mode of storage peculiar to maids and somehow repellent. But there it is. Paper handkerchiefs must be accumulated for family colds which seem less dreary when the handkerchief can be instantly burnt, leaving the victim unencumbered with a million germs crawling about on crushed linen.

Everyone is storing something: silk stockings; face cream; tins of beef. We have a goodly tinnery of sardines in the canteen larder, since even two small fishes will add piquancy to a pile of egg sandwiches. Miss Blossom casts her eyes to the ceiling and says :

" You should see what's tucked away down in the cellar. Looks like a tin mine down there; and you mark my words 'twill all go bad on us."

But bully beef will keep for five years—so the soldiers say. They ought to know.

" 'Tisn't right to take the food from other folks. We must all muck in when the bad days come. Look at the tea down there! Great chests of it." She turns over her ledger and inserts $11\frac{1}{2}d.$ in copperplate handwriting.

" But mind you," she continues, with a flash of loyalty, " it's difficult for Madam. We are all sorry for her. People won't abide by their rations. They want tea before breakfast, tea at breakfast, tea for tea, tea at bedtime. Can't be done on two ounces a week. They'd know quick enough if they were in their own homes."

Why do people expect miracles in hotels? Housekeeping has become so difficult in private houses that perhaps even a fortnight's freedom from it makes women go berserk and call for tea out of sheer passionate relief of knowing that someone else will get it for them.

Hotels cater, as a rule, for persons in their relaxed and baser states. But the permanent hotel resident is past redemption.

This attitude is quickly caught by the staff. Inconsequent maids fling solid tea-leaves down the drainpipes. The " boots " steals both coal and potatoes. Miss Blossom struggles to right these wrongs. But Madam cannot stiffen the organisation. Everything has sagged and slackened since Master died and Miss Blossom's attempted reforms annoy instead of galvanise the worried little widow.

Meanwhile she searches, feverishly, for a waiter. No one who has not tried to run a war-time household has any idea of how difficult it is. People must be fed and kept moderately clean; clothes washed, mended; meals prepared, washed up. And there is practically no one to help housewives. Only elderly women or girls of fifteen are available. Younger "dailies" now are all doing the work previously done by resident maids. Which is right, but there are limits to what one pair of hands can do.

If there are any servants to be had the hotels get them. Life there being more colourful, more full of change than in an ordinary household. And tips are the great attraction.

Yet even in this unhurried place, far from factories and the general atmosphere of war, maids are slow to come, quick to go. Many only stay a week. Each one seems less efficient than the last. None can do anything properly. Bed covers are always crooked, dusting skipped, sweeping neglected. The work has to be done somehow. Applicants are few; whoever can be found is caught. Few questions are asked. References belong to the dead, leisured past. No employer now writes or rings up those who are in a position to say if a housemaid is clean and honest. And in any case most references are but worthless scraps of paper. The personal interview is everything.

"Yes, Madam," says the just-seventeen-year-old maid to the hotel proprietress, "I am used to hard work, being the eldest of eight. I've nursed them through all their illnesses, and did for Mother, too, when they were born. And I looked after Granny when she had a miscarriage. So you see I'm very experienced." Vitality is obviously the family heritage. A priceless possession. But love of change accompanies it. Her stay is short. Perhaps Granny had another miscarriage.

Of course it is dull to sweep under somebody's bed when you are seventeen and the sun is shining and soldiers are loitering at street corners, making every sort of invitation.   Sickening to stop staring out of the window because number ten is ringing for morning tea and Mrs. Friske wants to know where her white sandals are.   Maddening to have to clean smart shoes when you haven't any yourself.   The bath is full of sand and the Hoover's broken and the man who ought to mend it is marching over a Middle Eastern desert (which is much fuller of sand than the bath) singing " Waltzing Matilda."

All manner of petty annoyances combine to irritate the maids, because food and clothes are their chief joys and the shortage of both increases.   Few domestic workers manage their pay or their wardrobes with good sense.   They waste their employer's goods and seldom learn thrift.

The staff food is badly managed, which quickly breeds discontent.   Food matters more than anything to physical workers. They give out a lot and must take in a lot.   The moral effect of good meals keeps them happy.   How embittering it must be to be given only rough bits left over from the dining-room.   Better one rasher cooked " especially for me" than a slice of turkey discarded by someone else.

No employer who fails to understand this can expect her establishment to run smoothly.

Brain workers seem to be above food.   They draw their strength from infinitely deeper sources.

When, at last, the turning wheels are stilled and the clamour of the factories dies away, what will happen to all the women war workers?   Our clever female M.P.s seem to share the same ideas. They encourage girls to seek employment outside the home, never within it.   Two wars have been fought by the men and women of our generation.   What for?   To keep British homes alive, secure, enduring.

Can't some woman with time and brains put the question of domestic service upon a new and fair basis, to the satisfaction of both employers and employed?

Already a new type of maid has appeared, the 194– model. Middle-aged in the last war, old in this, she sweeps into her own with the experience of a lifetime behind her.   Such a one has come to the Crescent Hotel.   She must have ceased worrying over trifles about 1880, judging by her cheerful face and snowy hair.

Tall, very round behind and before, fresh-faced Jenny looks and is the epitome of respectability.

With rare good taste, uncommon in the stout, she has her clothes made amply large, thereby balancing her bulk. Her curves undulate but never protrude. Full black shining skirts, flat black shoes ; a perfectly plain white apron of tombstone smoothness, unrelieved by even a button. Long plain strings are lost completely about the folds of her tubby waist, to emerge behind her in a stiff bow, with long ends fluttering as she moves. Immaculate cuffs, that appear to have been sliced off white marble, frame the old hands that are so deft.

Has she really got ankles, calves, knees under all that bunchy skirt that just misses the floor and gives her ungainly body a becoming air of dignity? She is, apparently, legless: just a skirt and feet. Like Mrs. Noah.

The cheeky waiter, whom she has replaced, has been called up for the Naval Reserve, where the life and language may be more to his taste.

"Better leave me clothes be'ind for the other chap," he bawls coarsely to Miss Blossom, who replies evenly, without raising her eyes from the ledger, "No, you needn't. He's a woman."

Jenny is a marvel, sweeping between the tables like a battle-cruiser, taking orders, waiting, clearing dishes with dexterity in spite of being built for comfort rather than speed. She looks like a fat, shining seal, threading her way about the dining-room's white cloths. Everyone beholding Jenny for the first time looks, inevitably, to see what kind of legs support this Mountain of Alpaca. They must be of the billiard-table variety; worth looking at. But all are doomed to disappointment. Up she floats like a mighty ship, with the strange grace that large things, expertly handled, have. All eyes fall floorwards. She has no legs. Only a skirt and feet.

Perhaps she "lifts off" like those monstrous dolls with which queer people covered up their telephones and nightgowns in the bad old days. Perhaps she has three legs instead of two; there may be something that she wants to hide. It remains a mystery, provoking, unsolved. Hands and face are all we ever see of Jenny. Her clothes seem to grow upon her, as moss covers a tree, or ivy a church tower—naturally. It is impossible to think of removing them, to conjecture upon what lies so deeply buried.

What an exacting life. Yet she looks happy. Everyone likes her, even the new daily housemaid who wears nothing but an overall, sandals, and a wedding-ring.

"My husband's at sea," she smiles.

Miss Blossom takes one look at her, sniffs, registering inwardly, "Portsmouth Streets." And the outgoing waiter runs his eyes over the girl, thinking, "Just my luck to be leaving now!"

Days are busy, but once the children are in bed all the dreariness of hotel life becomes startlingly apparent. The lounge is decorated, inoffensively, in green and cream. Madam has mercifully spared us, there, the garish colours which she sports upon her person. There is nothing definite to distract or dismay. The brass is bright, a fire is always generously provided on chilly days, and yet how cold and meaningless that room is. The figures in it seem straw-stuffed dummies rather than flesh and blood personalities. Many might well find sanctuary in a museum labelled, "This species is found only in English hotels." Mr. Friske reads a financial paper. His hat is beside him. He suggests going for a good blow over the cliffs, but his wife freezes him with a glance. They are to play bridge to-night. Mrs. Friske has never had a good blow in her life. The cobwebs of suburbia mist her heart and mind. Desultory shopping in crowded streets is all that she knows about fresh air.

So kind Mr. Friske sighs, gazes at the pageant of gold and amber slashed with crimson above the grape-coloured sea, and obediently fetches the card table. He looks at Mrs. Friske critically, for perhaps the first time in their long married life, and wishes she were young and gay; he is tired of her velvet-curtain-Turkey-carpet-wireless-and-cinema mentality. His childless home is little more than a comfortable prison, a cold place for all its central heating. With no beauty anywhere. The sight of Cornish sunsets, the feel of Cornish spray flying in his face, the sweep of tumbling waves, majestic, unconfined, has bred a hunger in his heart that his wife cannot satisfy. He glances, speculatively, at Miss Blossom's ample figure, stares at the pretty girls in their cheap, attractive finery, sauntering with impudent ease among the troops, and sighs behind his cards. He has never had his full romance ration.

Solitary females, in crêpe-de-chine, with untidy hair, turn over the old picture papers. The awful preponderance of well-to-do workless women is nowhere more apparent than here. Someone must have earned that weekly cheque that they pay for living expenses. It seems unlikely from their mien that they ever struggled for it themselves. Small wonder that they look blank, and bleak and bored. No spur of necessity has ever pricked them into activity. Safety First has been their motto.

It was impossible to marry Alec. They did not love him enough. How could they tell unless they tried? Hopeless to be a hospital nurse because mother said NO. And so life, the stinging nettle, has passed them by, because they lacked courage to grasp it. Unlike Miss Blossom and Mrs. Blunt, to whom every day is a battlefield strewn, often, with dead hopes, but nevertheless, the pride and joy of conflict is theirs.

It is cheering when livelier folk come to stay.

A soldier and his wife are here for a week. He is recovering from wounds. She is gay, amusing, friendly. " Ah! Pollyon has a quality of its own. You'll love it; I was born near by and always want to come back. It's the air. Is Isobel still here? She was one of Freddy Fenshaw's girls. He set her up in a beauty business when his wife got difficult, bought that little cream and scarlet house for her. And now he's just been killed."

" Poor Isobel. Ghastly for her to be washing and waving women's hair! He gave her a marvellous time before the war. She kept him longer than any of them. He spent all his war leave with her down here. He'd never looked at a girl over twenty-two and Isobel is thirty-five."

So Lady Fenshaw is left without husband or child or lover, alone, save for the vast wealth with which she tried to buy Freddy. It was her money that paid for the shop in Pollyon High Street, where the woman who loved Freddy for himself counts up her daily takings, wondering just how long she can hang on.

Her words come back to me as she cuts Sally's hair. " Yes, business is difficult. Hotels are full, but there are no young women here. I hope to be ambulance driving very soon."

The little town then has its secrets, unguessed, undreamed of. Passion flowers have lived their short life about the small stone house, and a man walked out of that bravely painted cream and scarlet door into the shadows. Perhaps as they gathered about him he saw Pollyon again—dreaming above the curved bay: a place of everlasting peace.

At day's end, tea, which brings some women together in a mysterious way, is brought into the lounge. They gather like starlings about the tray, sipping, chatting, giggling. My little green and white room is a welcome refuge from public places. The big multi-coloured work-basket from Colombo is always full of mending. Broken elastic, stretched to capacity over fast-growing bodies, missing buttons, demanding instant attention, but not, alas, Master's socks. A pile of ironing must be dealt with and there stands the neglected typewriter, an uncomfortable rebuke. All these cry: " Me first! Me first!" A row of shoes need cleaning. For a week I put them hopefully outside, but there was no getting them back for breakfast. After much ado they were sent up all soaked with hastily applied whitening, and quite unfit for wear. It's less trouble to do them myself.

But to-night the children have " done a surprise." The whitening saucer, overflowing with water, stands on the floor, and beside it three pairs of well-moistened shoes are triumphantly arrayed. Greyish smears on Baby's rosy sleeping face prove that she has played her part in cleaning activities.

" From all these operations our daughters have safely returned."

How the pleasant tangle of home life is missed. Even on a short holiday housewives have a half-guilty feeling of desertion. The lovely network of threads that binds them to house, garden, family and the general roundabout of living is, temporarily, broken. The most commonplace incidents serve to remind her of this. Here there is no room to keep buttons or elastic or letters. If safety-pins or paste or paper clips are urgently wanted no frenzied searchings can reveal them, because they all stayed at home with the fat dictionary that is sorely missed when awkward words like embarrass or apparel have to be set down on paper, correctly.

All the right-sounding words like albatross, vainglory, rumbustious and amaranthine are easy to spell. But they are not written so often as their duller fellows. More's the pity.

Oh, for the hall drawer, with its brown paper, string, little cardboard boxes, labels and rubber bands. Here, labels live a mile off. It's strange to be without all these props.

At home every day has its own individuality. Tiny happenings mark it out from its fellows. Grind, the gardener, comes on Thursdays and Fridays and is then responsible for bringing in vegetables, carting wood, putting dry kindling ready for the kitchen boiler, emptying the pig bucket, sweeping the garage, all the outdoor jobs which are usually mine. This enables me to give one entire morning to family mending. When everything is rather old repairing assumes vast proportions. The second morning is devoted to household shopping.

On Tuesdays, Sally's dancing tunic and slippers must be packed in her schoolbag; and the baker brings deliciously new doughnuts on that afternoon, sugary balls, waiting for the onslaught of little pearly teeth. Sunday lunch had a meaning all its own. It was the one meal of the week when we were all together and something special was produced as a " Surprise." Four pansy-blue eyes were eagerly glued to the door, waiting to see what Alice would carry in. It was always something different.

Golden cutlets, encircled with mashed potato, peas, carrots. How a child loves the colour of food; creamy junket, topped with scintillating scarlet jelly. Or turkey, on a lordly dish; Stilton for Nick, and cheese straws, piled high, criss-cross, pagoda fashion. And afterwards little eager fingers, and bigger, slower ones, would rummage in a box of sweets. Then the long afternoon, stretched at peace in the quiet, scented garden, with rooks, calling, calling; or, in winter, before a log fire, drowsily content reading to Sue. . . . "And then God made a man." "Did He? Good gwacious, what for?" All that has gone, vanished like a dream. Here and now each day is like the other. Morning, afternoon, evening, night melt into a slowly turning wheel of jumbled hours. The whole time-table of living has gone askew; known milestones have disappeared.

But, happily, the children's needs remain and increase. Daily lessons keep us busy. They keep me much busier than the pupils, because it is not easy to teach a child of nine when you have never

been to school yourself.   The intricacies of Long Division confuse
me still; we go on and on covering sheets of paper with serpent-
like tails, and the worm turns . . . over the page.   Having battled
through life without any knowledge of fractions it's fearful to be
faced with them now.   Mathematics can only be taught by experts.
That fact emerges clearly from Mamma's chaotic mind, so she
sticks to what she knows—the geography of the places where she
has lived, and the dramatic Bible stories, superbly told in the old
way that is always new, and the songs and poems and fairy tales
of an everlasting beauty that time cannot dim.   Geography is easy
to teach—interesting to learn.   You can see it all at a glance.   The
great shining map, many-coloured countries, huge breadths of
sea.   A child enjoys studying something that it can see and
handle.

"Look!   There's Canada!   Where Valerie is.   She sailed from
Liverpool over the Atlantic.   India is here.   I took you there when
you were twelve weeks old, through the Red Sea; it was so hot
everyone had prickly heat, but you slept all night."

"And here is Hong Kong, where no one was ever old or tired
or sad.   A place of almost blinding beauty.   Uncle Val is there
still."

You can't see history like that.   It's thrilling to read of Henry
the Eighth executing his wives, but you can't point to them and
say: "This is Anne Boleyn's head" as you can say: "This is Germany, where Hitler lives (or lived).   That's Dunkirk, where
Daddy's got his D.S.O.   Now let's find Sheffield where nail
scissors are made."

It's fun to learn about ships, tanks, seagulls, crabs, flowers, things
that have life, colour or movement, and which play a part in
daily life.

Stories of Granny's youth, though lacking in educational value,
fascinate Sally because they are true.   Her eyes widen to hear that
Granny once stamped and shouted "Six years old and pegged in
a nursery!"   That spirit buoyed her up across eighty stormy
years.   Most of us could do with more of it.

Sue, happily, is still at THE CAT IS ON THE MAT stage.   Long may
they both remain there.   But she won't.   Alas!   Alas! she will
have to be imprisoned in a classroom confronted with all the
bewildering paraphernalia of learning.   Soon her busy feet and

the fast-fleeting months will bring her to childhood's threshold. She will run over it laughingly, but one of the loveliest things in life will die when that day dawns, and a baby is lost for ever.

Chapter IV

THE CANTEEN

THE CANTEEN IS NOW A GOING CONCERN. MANY IMPROVEMENTS
are being made. The one large room becomes uncomfortably
congested so another new one is allotted to us. It has been cluttered
for months with the bones, tins, and papers of Pollyon, awaiting
the reluctant dustman. These national treasures are now housed
elsewhere.

Two of us spend a day cleaning the windows, washing the floor,
brushing out cupboards. Furniture has been given. A green
velvet divan, with a wickedly alluring air, comes from the Bull
Hotel; a faint aroma of scent and cigars clings to it. The slightly
tarnished richness of the cushions is utterly out of place in this bare
apartment, but soldiers who have walked nine miles will sit thankfully upon anything.

Open the windows. Let Pollyon's glorious air sweep away all
contacts with the Bull lounge.

A dart-board, comfortable writing-table and several easy-chairs have also been presented, together with a handsome rug of violently Oriental design. We invade the W.V.S. headquarters hoping to scrounge some curtains, but Mrs. Blunt shoos us away, fearful lest we rob her of shirt material for many little boys. She has spare curtains at home and will bring them to-morrow.

This small room looks on to Pollyon High Street, a supreme advantage, as the sight of soldiers sitting there, drinking tea, laughing and looking at home, is the best possible advertisement for our trade. The tiny canteen entrance leading to the big back inner room looks frowsty, forbidding. But now we can put our goods into the shop window, trade is doubled.

Not all our clients come from nine miles distant. Some are less than half that. Many nearer.

Sometimes the rooms get so full it seems as if the walls must bulge. Black boots, brown hands, red faces, press against the narrow counter, a warm flood of humanity waiting to be fed. We work on alternate shifts: one day in the kitchen, the next day waiting. It is a welcome change to serve teas after the eternal slicing and sluicing of scullery life. Pleasant to leave the opening of salmon tins, the cutting of crumbling bread to other hands sometimes. To watch the men's faces as they eat, read, talk and joke. To hear their scraps of conversation, to learn, more and more, what the British Army really is.

Gradually the various characters strengthen and stand out. There is the slim R.A.F. sergeant, who comes in every Tuesday about two o'clock when trade is slack. The formula never varies.

" May I leave these here?" he asks diffidently, handing a thick volume over the counter, and retaining a booklet. " My Post Office Savings account; I like to put a little in every week. It makes a lot to carry as I'm shopping for the fellars who are on duty."

" What a heavy book to bring so far."

He laughs, rather awkwardly. " It's a dictionary. I'm trying to educate myself a bit—left school early."

" Two poached eggs and tea?" His usual order.

" Please."

He rummages among the papers, selects a shilling weekly, pores over the letterpress, head on hands, lost in a bigger world. When the food is set before him he eats fast, absent-mindedly, his eyes fascinated by the printed page. Two cups of tea. Slice of cake. Then he pays and disappears, returning later for the dictionary. When pretty Miss Jolly is on duty he stays for further refreshment, lingers at the counter, prolonging the business of his simple purchases. Once he even forgot his dictionary, but he was learning something more precious than can be found on any printed page.

Spike and Ginger Scot are most regular patrons. Spike goes first to Daisy's cage. Bird and man regard each other with deep, silent interest. She watches him approach, lifting her claws up and down, up and down, as if making dough with deliberate movements, sure sign that she is pleased.

Ginger Scot, who is more social than Spike, threads his way among the tables, greeting pals on every side. Ginger Scot and Spike only understand each other's speech with difficulty; they argue and wrangle, never agree about anything, and yet some curious bond links them together. They are fast friends. Spike for all his slowness of speech, has a shrewder tongue and brain. Like all true countrymen he is independent in thought and action. His character and personality are rooted in the width and peace and comfort of his native Oxfordshire fields.

Alf the Cockney, is often attached to them; a true Londoner who will chatter like a starling to anyone. There is no need to look up or smile and speak when Alf comes in. Listeners hold no interest for him. He only wants to hear his own voice.

"Very nice the food 'ere, very nice it is, very nice indeed, lidy, and we appreciate 'avin' somewhere to set down. It's fine, but I wish we could 'ave fish suppers, think we could, lidy, fish suppers, you know, fish and chips, jist Fridays and Saturdays, that would be fine that would . . ." his voice trails on and on. . . .

He's right. It would be fine. But how can we do it for sixty to a hundred men? Impossible! The stove is too small, and fat is scarce. Yet his suggestion fires a train of thought. Tea, tea, tea. Every day. How tired the men must get of it. Why not soup for a change at night? Perhaps volunteers could make it in their own homes. There's no room here.

We talk it over. Ask the men. Soup? Yes, good idea. Plenty of onion! Thanks, we'd like it. That would be fine!

So huge quantities of bones are bought from the butcher, which produce enough stock to drown a person in. Onions, carrots, peas, pearl barley are willingly contributed and added. Each week-end the canteen helpers stagger in with this savoury liquid in bowls and bottles. We heat and sell it with astonishing rapidity.

" Saturday night is soup night," chants Alf, demanding a third cup. It is so popular that we provide it on Fridays as well. The soup is delicious and the enjoyment it gives is worth any trouble. But washing eighty soupy cups takes twice as long as if tea had been drunk. The rich meaty flavour, so nourishing and pleasant, leaves thick grease in the china mugs.

So they must be wiped with paper. Every civilised woman wipes greasy plates before committing them to the sink.

" It's waste of time wiping those mugs," remarks Mrs. Treloon, who is merely looking on with knitting for " our boys" in her clean hands.

" It takes longer to clean the sink if we don't wipe them," smiles Mrs. Blunt, " and last week the drainpipe was stopped up with grease. We can't get a plumber now, they've all been called up, and we can't do it ourselves, because we have no tools."

If we had not wiped the cups Mrs. Treloon would have suggested that we should. Her mind works that way. She is the typical Little Town Personage. Perhaps some day she will take a trip round the world and discover that she is just Nobody At All. She'd like to turn the traffic lights on Broadway green if they were red, and red if they were green.

Mrs. Blunt is like a channel through which all experience sweeps, unhindered, a sweetening, satisfying process. Mrs. Treloon's mentality is of the roundabout variety—everything revolves in perfect order but finds no outlet.

In the front room conversation is all male. Loud, often monosyllabic, sometimes even brusque; short sentences casually flung out, casually answered, yet always full of warmth and laughter for all its lack of noise. There is a tremendous under-current of vitality in the men's deep voices that buzz so pleasantly. No shrillness, no sense of hurry about them, yet all the fierce fire of youth can be felt and heard in every word they say. So that even when we cannot see their strong bodies, thick necks, broad hands and cheerful weather-beaten faces, we are conscious of that great tide of life that sweeps through them.

How different is the female talk behind the hatch; high-toned, ceaseless, and questioning. Soldiers never question; they have learnt to obey orders.

But the task of washing up is enriched by listening to the chattering helpers. The writer of any woman's page could glean enough here to fill her columns for many a week. One of the main topics is How to Feed Husbands in War-time, a problem that calls for more mental and culinary agility with each passing month.

" Ever tried him with carrot pudding?"

" No, how do you make it?"

Details follow.

" You try him with that."

The unfortunate husband seems to be in much the same position as Daisy the parrot who is " tried" by every manner of morsel. But her appetite never overcomes her discrimination. She stares, sniffs, recoils, advances, stops to think the matter over, tastes with the utmost caution and suddenly spits out anything that is not exactly to her taste. Perhaps " he" will treat the carrot pudding likewise.

" Fish?" Mrs. Treloon is speaking. " Who could eat fish when you think of what's going on in the sea?"

" You mean the risk fishermen run to get it?"

" No! No! It's what the fish feed on. German sailors!" A pleasing rather than a revolting thought to true patriots.

" Oatmeal—now he won't touch it for breakfast. But I give it him in the soup. Never knows, drinks it up and says ' That's lovely.' Must have something hot before he goes off with the Home Guard."

" I get home before that lot comes out. Real dangerous they are with their rook rifles and revolvers and half of them never fired a shot for twenty years."

The local Home Guard certainly carry a formidable assortment of weapons. The thermos caps protruding from their pockets were at first taken for steel truncheons until finally shown to be harmless receptacles for refreshment. All agree that the night-duty policeman stands in grave danger from being attacked by over-zealous volunteers.

Another voice breaks in: " My son, he never could stand the Army. He'd come home on leave, sit down and cry and cry and cry. ' I can't stand it, Mother; I'll never go back.' "

" What can't he stand, the sergeant?"

" He never said. It's just the Army. Then he went to Shanghai. That's far away and very hot. It seemed to acclimatise him a bit. He liked that. Then Dunkirk. 'Thank God for the Navy.' That was all he said when he come home. After a bit he told us what had happened.

" Run," says he, " never run so fast in all my life as I did then. There I was throwin' my goods into the ditches. Lord! I did run. Twenty-six miles."

A new light upon the greatest fighting retreat of all time.

His mother stops for breath. She is thin, worn, almost without flesh, just a bunch of bones.

" But I've been lucky. I've had two husbands. Lost 'em both ; good chaps they were. But I still have my boy. He's got three nice children. They stayed with me for a week but drove me fair crazy. I'm tired now, can't stand racket."

She is plain. Poor. Old. Yet the full cycle of experience has been hers. Two men cared for her. She has a son. Grandchildren. Many women have had less from life.

A wistful note creeps into her brisk voice. "I like to cum here and listen to these lads laugh. It's quiet at home, all alone; nuthin' to do fur anyone now."

Up goes the hatch, a mass of crockery shovelled through for washing.

" Silk stockings? Did you say they were made from old sausage skins, or are the sausage skins made from old silk stockings?"

Thank Heaven we don't " do" sausages here. The consuming public turns from one shut door to beat upon another. If sweetened tea is no longer available then cigarettes must take its place. As they grow scarce, odd cups of coffee during the day are substituted until milk becomes difficult. Finally all are abandoned.

As more troops come into, or near, the little town, catering difficulties increase. The Royal West Hamptonshires marched through Pollyon to-day. The modern infantryman is rushed about in lorries and buses. He may even learn to drop from parachutes: his uniform is different and yet at heart he remains the same. Nothing can ever really change the British infantryman with his rifle, his bayonet and his own unfaltering feet.

In the end every battle is won by British infantrymen with

rifles and bayonets. The sight of them off parade stirs the heart and catches the imagination as deeply as fifty thousand British and Indian troops sweeping past the saluting base on the 'Pindi parade ground. Not all the splendour of old-time cavalry, with their gleaming hides, silvery bits and spurs, their sense of speed and picturesqueness could ever dim the magic that hangs about a column on the march. Even in peace all stand and stare to watch them pass and wish them well. And in war the tragic significance of those swinging bodies is intensified tenfold.

When again will troops march back into their county town, with all the flags flying to welcome them? When again will they hear their regimental march burst with triumph as they swing into those red barrack walls that shelter so many for a little while?

These newcomers are slow to patronise our canteen. Perhaps the sight of hardened warriors there somewhat alarms them. But Spike, now my firm friend, brings a gawky boy in one day and pushes him towards the counter saying by way of introduction:

" 'E comes from Oxfordshire. Same as me. Water Eaton."
So he knows Hampton Poyle, with the lovely stretch of river behind Kidlington Church and the grey-green willows, so graceful and sad, sweeping down to the lush grass all dappled with wild flowers.

The boy's huge hands lie with awkward idleness among the littered cups and buns. His boots are too tight; his arms and neck all hot and tickly from the rough constricting khaki. He finds that he is never alone, and yet never has the company for which he craves. The Army is like that. He longs to sit in socks and shirt-sleeves eating sausages and reading the sporting page, with his dog at his feet and the sound of farm horses in the yard outside.

The bare barrack room, so sparsely equipped, yet seething with humanity, almost terrifies him. The ceaseless chatter, communal feeding and sleeping are unknown horrors to this farmer's son used to long hours alone in fields. He looks, and feels, caged. He ought to be carting hay now in the green elm-shadowed pastures where he and Spike and I were bred, his body stripped to the sun, instead of standing here among all these buns sweltering under that uniform, which he will grow to love. The time will quickly come when he feels that he has always been a soldier and that it is the best of all lives. The Army is like that.

He has found a friend in Spike. The land links all her lovers together and I, too, feel less lonely watching and hearing them, less aware of all the absurd and pathetic snobbery of a little town.

The fields near Spike's home have names according to their characteristics. Full Bag Field. Poor Field slopes northward from the sun. Forty Acre. Rushy Moor. Ghost Green. A ruined cottage flanked by yews stands on Ghost Green and even in high summer there is something sinister about the silence of the deep grass there. Owls hoot about the crumbling stones at twilight and few villagers will pass there after dusk.

Stilly Copse is a cluster of trees where two farms meet. A man was found murdered there years ago. There is no footpath through it. No bird song breaks the deathlike silence of that place.

Little does Spike know that he has made these half-forgotten memories live again in someone's heart. There he sits on the green velvet sofa from the Bull Hotel, comfortably weary, staring at the cheerful clatter in the High Street, nodding to his friends as they come in.

How can our portals be improved? Could the door be painted scarlet or cream? But that might only emphasise the deplorable shabbiness of the surroundings and the house would look like a woman who cares for her face but neglects her neck.

The steps have been whitened; that's an improvement, but the flagged passage beyond them is still grim, uninviting, a slur upon the establishment.

It must be cleaned. Scrubbing is hard, skilled work. Many people might snort to hear such a lowly occupation described as skilled. Let them tackle it, if they never have. That there is a right and wrong way of scrubbing soon becomes painfully obvious to the beginner. None of us are experts. We have all tried and failed. Scrubbing is hard work. No matter what the procedure the stones still remain murky and the vigorously plied brush merely whisks out grains of long-lost dust from between the cracks, which mingle, maddeningly, with the surface dirt. All is swept into a bucket of black water which in spite of constant refillings remains dark as a tropical pool.

The passage is a sloping one. How to tackle it? Uphill? Downhill? Sideways? The dirty water either runs rapidly into our knees or cascades in the opposite direction, out of control. And sweeping is not enough. Once a week that entrance must be scrubbed. The British flag hangs there. It cannot be disgraced. Then one day a small white-haired woman appears with a coarse apron and bucket. She takes a brush, pail and soap and in twenty minutes cleanliness reigns.

" How did you do it?"

She smiles, toothlessly. " 'Tis just use. Dun it all my life."

" Would you like some tea?"

" I'd be glad of it."

This is a treasure who must not be lost. She only asks a shilling an hour payment and in half that time she makes the passage a shining highway.

" Can't she come weekly for two hours to ' clean us up'?"

" We have a great many expenses," hedges Mrs. Treloon.

Have we, what are they? The food is paid for by the men who eat it. Kind Mr. Jolly gives the premises. Soap, teacloths, crockery, bowls, knives have all been gladly contributed. All of us would thankfully pay a shilling or two to have the entrance passage and the Gent's Cloak scrubbed efficiently every week.

" Of course it must be done," says the Duchess firmly, and since she is the greatest among us that settles it. " We can't fall below barrack-room standards."

" By the winter we'll get hot baths going on Fridays and Saturdays. Meanwhile they can bathe."

" They've no bathing clothes."

" Does that matter?"

" Someone might be stupid enough to think so."

" Well, we've collected a house and crockery and furniture and a velvet sofa and about a thousand men. We might collect pants too."

The Duchess's lovely face is lit with amused interest. She opens her notebook. Begins to write. Both she and Mrs. Blunt have the common touch. They instinctively recognise the needs of humanity and endeavour to supply them. No one is ever awkward in their company. They have a sort of warmth that eases and oils all the prickles of canteen life. And there are many.

Someone uses too much disinfectant for the sink and the Gent's Cloak; another has burnt the only aluminium saucepan. The tea ration is not going round. Three spoonfuls for the blue pot, four for the brown. Of course. Of course. No one has ever been guilty of using more. Grown women pipe up their answers like fear-ruled Victorian children.

Who leaves the lids off the bread tins at night, thereby reducing new loaves into unusable offal? Nobody knows. All stare helplessly at each other with mild surprise, protesting their innocence as scullery maids do when questioned by the cook. Are the cups and saucers to be set out as such, complete with spoon, or are cups and saucers to be piled separately, and quickly paired as wanted? Which is the quickest method during rush hours? Opinions differ.

Some suggest that all tea should be poured out in the kitchen and put through the hatch. Others say No, the sight of cups and a teapot on the counter is a welcoming and homely touch not to be forfeited for mere speed of service. Anything that stands for home, comfort and peace must be cherished.

Sentiment plays a big part in the soldier's outlook. Let us keep to the old symbols and if an urn must be bought, it can be secreted and used solely for replenishing purposes, and not for individual pouring. Who wants a drink out of something that looks like a baby gasometer?

Then the spoons are too large. They overbalance and crash upon the floor as the tea is handed out. Table covers, floor and Government trousers are splashed. This gives an impression of indifference and carelessness which is distressing. The bread is always too new, or too stale. Like women, who are invariably too young or too old for everything. You can't make sandwiches from warm dough nor yet from loaves which shout two days before yesterday.

All the doughnuts are eaten first while buns are left. They can be, and are, toasted—but the cake? On Fridays and Saturdays everything goes—nothing but plates and crumbs are left, yet food must be provided for Mondays and Tuesdays if only for a dozen men. Time and again have I run up Pollyon High Street with a bare loaf in each hand while Mrs. Treloon is dissecting sardines like a first-class surgeon performing his favourite operation, or she is bashing up eggs with extraordinary skill and vigour, for waiting soldiers who haven't come for ten Mondays and won't again.

How good-natured soldiers are; models of good manners and good feeling, never grumbling at the unavoidable wait, grateful for what comes. They seem to understand the difficulty of catering for unknown numbers without waste. It's always " May I have . . .?" or " Are there any . . .?" Never an abrupt demand. They don't bark as the Crescent Hotel visitors do, when the inadequate staff are a bit slow in handing the potatoes. Black looks don't follow us as we scuttle round. Thanks are always given for the very smallest service.

What gentlemen they are. A nation is judged by its humour or lack of it. A woman by her hats. A man by his manners. Why are men's manners so much better than women's? Watch them in a hotel or café. They invariably say " Good morning " to the waitress who serves them. Women never do that. And as there are no pretty waitresses left that increases the value of politeness. All the self-elected beauties joined the Forces long ago.

Why is it we understand each other so well yet find the excellent Mrs. Treloon, and some of her friends, full of awkward corners? Why does she want to be different from what she is? Why can't she be happy with Mr. Treloon, her pretty daughter, thriving business, and smart comfortable home? What more does she want and why?

She has great possessions yet values none of them. These soldiers have nothing except their own stout hearts and each other. They treat triumph and disaster both the same. Perhaps therein lies the secret of their strength and their invincibility. Their very presence is stimulating. How could anyone ever lose heart in the face of the Army's unfailing cheerfulness? It's as much a part of them as their boots and buttons. It might almost be described as " Issue" except that it needs no replenishing from the Quartermaster's stores or the War Office or wherever their uniform comes from. And how infectious their lightheartedness is.

Exhausted men and women, robbed of sleep night after night, unfold their papers as they hurry to a new day's work. The brightest pages of all British history is written there.

" . . . Throughout the week the Germans have bombed Malta every night, using large-scale machine-gunning and bombing indiscriminately in every direction. The people are calm."

" Thirty-eight survivors of a British ship torpedoed by a German raider off the African coast have endured the horrors of twenty-two days in an open boat . . . forty others were at sea for thirteen days with no food and no water . . . The terrible and superbly brave story is revealed in a message from Brazil. Eighty-two men, including the Captain and many Indians, were loaded into a boat built for fifty-eight and headed for South America with a small mainsail and jib. Four British and forty Indians died. The Captain refused to give up. He guided the boat to within sight of the Brazilian coast and then died saying: ' All's well.' "

And on another page " Killed on duty at her post, beloved wife of Officer Cadet . . . mother of Tom and Jill, aged twenty-two. . . ."

Again, " In spite of all his endeavours the enemy has nowhere penetrated our line . . ."

The very baldness of the statements double their horror and glory. The significance of all else pales before those poignant words. It is incomprehensible that flesh and blood can endure so much. Tired, elderly men and women forget their fatigue, the effort of lashing on tired bodies that must, must do the work of younger people and something of the soldier's spirit blossoms in their hearts. They catch and share, if only for one brief moment, the far-off splendour that is his. They are with him. They can see what he sees, hear what he hears, almost feel what he feels. His sacrifice, his agony stiffens their resistance, gives them new power to go on.

Do the men of Dunkirk, Narvik, Greece, Crete, Libya, realise just how much they mean to the men and women in the street? Do they know that thousands of women with aching hearts and limbs, trying to keep a home together on almost nothing at all for someone who may never come back, listen to the news of these British battles, and are given fresh courage to fight their own?

Do soldiers understand all this? Couldn't somebody tell them? Has anyone outside the Army ever loved the British private as Kipling did?

There are days when the canteen menu unavoidably fails to supply his favourite tit-bits which is bitter indeed for those who now know and try to plan for his tastes. He never shows disappointment, but we hate to see him having to take the inevitable cake when savoury snacks should have been forthcoming. There is so little that strangers can do for a man who is away from his wife, his village, or town, his favourite pub or cinema, garden, or football ground except to give him something nice to eat, and when that fails. . . .

During one Friday night flurry when a hundred and twenty men are squashed into the canteen a bottle of lemonade is upset over a plate of egg sandwiches. Those six eggs had been ordered and carefully saved for the week-end rush. Mayonnaise, margarine, milk had been beaten up with them to stretch their capacity to the uttermost limit, and a dozen men are waiting for them, cash in hand.

Well, there's one thing we can do when the war's over, and that's lose our tempers, if only for a second. Wonderful to be able to let go with a clear conscience. It's unpatriotic and absurd to do so now, when all must think of national and not personal difficulties even though a dozen privates have lost their supper and our shoes are full of lemonade. War is made the excuse for all kinds of slackness. The canteen milkman, who is habitually late, says he can't help it because he's in the A.F.S., which is, of course, of much greater importance than delivering milk. But all his fire-fighting duties are done in the evening between six and ten o'clock. That doesn't interfere with his milk round at 2.30 the following day, and Mrs. Blunt says he has been " behind the clock" for fifteen years. However, his explanations are not open to argument at the moment. The country must have firemen. Milk can wait. True enough, let it go at that. But the time will come when he can be, deservedly, blamed.

Sometimes provisions, men and helpers all arrive at the right time. There is enough of everything and customers can be instantly served exactly to their liking. Kindly folks bring in newspapers and flowers, and on such days perfection peak seems infinitely nearer.

And then suddenly out of one catastrophic day romance is born. Everything goes wrong. The bread has not come but the men have. Being early-closing day hastily purchased cakes are not available to fill the gap.

Suddenly the Air Force Sergeant looks out of the window and sees Miss Jolly's pretty pink face and yellow hair all damp and curly in the rain. She twists the larder door handle backwards and forwards many times. Her efforts are useless. Frustrated, she picks up the empty milk jug, and turns away. Then the airman forgets his education, his savings book, his fragrant tea. In a moment he is beside her. Luckily for him the door remains fast with all the weekly rations firmly behind it. When at last the lock is forced they vanish into the larder and there they stay. Luckily no one calls for the dairy produce. So the lovers are undisturbed, inside the slate-lined cubby-hole.

His poached eggs harden and grow cold before the hastily thrust-back chair.

The tea, so fresh at time of pouring, grows filmed, tasteless. " He'll want some more," says the Duchess, who sees everything without appearing to, slipping pence from her own bag into the till. The eggs won't be wasted, they can be pounded up with sardines for sandwiches. Farmer Jolly's pig will munch the toast with relish. Only the tea is thrown away.

How long does a man take proposing? We have forgotten, but in any case it is an awkward business and food is welcome after emotional crises. Five; ten; fifteen minutes. Long enough for any question to be answered. Crack, crack. Two more eggs are broken, dropped into the poachers. They begin to heat and curl at the edges. Good ! Here he comes, quiet as ever. The eggs are placed before him. He eats them, pays, walks out. While Miss Jolly wipes up the cups with an " I'll think it over" air. It takes more than a man in the larder to upset her calm efficiency.

They are well matched, bright-haired, blue-eyed. How lovely their children will be, pure, definite types, instead of the drab colourings that emerge from blonde and brunette unions.

After this happy interlude the day straightens. Out comes the sun in all his glory to dry the dishcloths. Once (it seems like a hundred years) I wanted the sun because someone was coming to lunch and we loved Norney Rough to look its best for our friends; or because Nick was playing golf with Jimmy Yates at Puttenham; or because we had to wash and dry Sally's hair quickly for her birthday party. Now dishcloths have replaced all that. Whenever the sun shines now I think of millions of women all over the world hanging out dishcloths.

The baker arrives and we slice up the loaves, mellowed by the presence of romance, our hearts back in the past remembering when it all happened to us . . . long ago.

Perhaps the Air Force Sergeant was suddenly overwhelmed with an intense longing for something of his own. So little is a man's own in the Services, only things like razors, letters and his thoughts. Even the food that is put before him belongs to the State. So does his shirt. He can't choose his tie or his cap. He can't come into a room, look round and say " Everything here is mine" in the way that the humblest cottager can.

He must be in his camp or barracks at a certain hour. At what age can a soldier disregard " Lights Out" with impunity? Even Generals, coupled with bad bridge partners, have been known to fake a yawn behind their hands and say, " Well, it's my bedtime," when the day's last bugle sounds.

So his emotions are almost the only thing that the fighting man can call his own. Small wonder then that they are strong and that the Air Force Sergeant suddenly longs to strengthen his position by adding pretty Miss Jolly to his dictionary and his savings book.

It is this wish for something of their own that fills the canteen because it is more pleasurable to make your own choice between two buns than meekly to accept whatever is put before you— which is the Army way. One man, at any rate, has found his soul mate here as well as a fairly wide selection of sandwiches, which is most cheering.

There is something touching about the soldier's lack of posses- sions. It puts him in the ranks of children, who always want everything but so seldom have the courage to ask for or the means to obtain it. Maybe that's why he is so lovable. He seems to have nothing at all. And can't even swim in nothing. Worse still, he has no pants that might do duty for a swim suit. And to confess to that would be a sort of emotional Dunkirk, a tearing down of something that must, at all costs, be preserved. His independence.

The heat is great. They are all hotly hooked up in this unbut- toned weather, though the most destitute evacuees from East London are floundering in a cool sea wearing somebody's pants.

Bathe? Yes, of course they'd love to, then why not? Haven't got a swim suit. Can't they go in without one? Absurd that they shouldn't when miles of unfrequented beach stretch in both direc- tions. There is no Mayor in Pollyon and surely only mayors trimmed with fur and a gold necklet arrest nude bathers on their sacred sands. In any case couldn't all Pollyon agree " not to look" while a thousand overheated men cool their war-worn bodies in the sweetest of all embraces?

" Can't afford swim suits." Well, there are shillings in our pockets, and " trunks" in Treloons, not a thousand pairs—far from it—however, a beginning might be made.

Are all soldiers poor? Surely not. Some are bachelor sergeants, and therefore comparatively rich; the matter is a delicate one. It's impossible to question a man who merely comes in to buy his tea from strangers. What should we think of a waitress who asked us if we possessed a dressing-gown? The position is similar. Yet some people think they can pry into a soldier's business just because he is a soldier. An odious error.

But something is arranged. Swim suits are bought by those who are glad to provide them; and a notice is hung up which can be either read or disregarded without any embarrassment of questioning. So a need is filled. The men change in the Gent's Cloak. Run down the fifty steps to the beach with trousers and tunic pulled over the communal trunks, towel in hand. We dry their wet things when they come back. It makes them feel that somebody cares. And it would please their mothers.

Chapter V

THE EVACUEES

THE LITTLE TRAIN COMES IN BACKWARDS READY TO GO OUT FACE
first. It puffs and pants up the long hill with its strange load. The
doors burst open and children pour into Pollyon. Another six
hundred. Scores came yesterday; fresh batches are due next week.

They seep across the platform, blackening it in ever-widening
circles. It is as if a giant hand had stirred up an ant's nest, and loosed
a swarm of little creatures to run helter-skelter in all directions with
rabbit-like speed and purposelessness. They tumble out of the car-
riages, hands cluttered with gas masks, iron rations, and further
impeded by the clutching fingers of someone even smaller than
themselves. Their eyes are wide with wonder; legs cramped by
the long journey, throats dry, hearts and minds overwhelmed,
bewildered.

One bumps against Sally as we pass the station, yelling: "You
with the Paddington lot?"

We are all with the Paddington lot. It is impossible to get away
from them. Pollyon is swamped with Londoners. Children flood
the pavements, wander about the streets, scamper over the sands,

their clustered bodies staining its goldness with dark swiftly-moving clots. They climb over railings, peer through shop windows, fall down steps, loiter in doorways. They stumble and scream and chatter in every house and garden, like flocks of chickens blissfully free from authoritative restraint.

Mites of a few summers stagger about unattended, escaping disaster at every turn, while their elder brothers and sisters dangle near the cliff edges with sickening unconcern.

A few are clean and tidy; the majority are filthy, with greyish-white faces betokening embedded dirt and malnutrition. Bare toes protrude from boots, or the bits of canvas that are tied on to their feet with shoelaces; the seats of shorts are torn, displaying either brownish lining beneath or unwashed skin. Their hair is matted. The lid has been lifted off London. Now we see what lies beneath.

The clean Cornish folk stare at this ragged, shrill community with mingled pity and apprehension. These are no trippers who come for a day, a week, and leave holiday litter to mar their welcome departure. But pitiable poverty-stricken refugees, seeking shelter for an indefinite period. They may already be orphans; their tragic homes a tangle of broken bricks. And the sight of this human flood brings home to Pollyon, with dramatic and belated suddenness, the full horror of war.

Until ten days ago one of the chief charms of Pollyon was its extraordinary stillness, due perhaps to its complete absence of trees. No flickering foliage disturbed the utter tranquillity of these quiet streets, no rippling, rustling leaves made movement against the still, stone walls.

But now a tide of humanity surges against them more insistent, more vital, more penetrating even than the long Atlantic rollers when they overflow their bounds. It seems as if voices say : " Let us in! Let us in!"

Houseproud spinsters, with a smart spare room and front parlour that let well in bygone Augusts, elderly couples, now bereft of family cares, and younger women, already overdone with olive branches, are faced with the clamour of slumland in their homes. Shouting, stamping hordes descend upon them.

Though slum dwellers far outnumber other visitors, there are well-to-do childern here too, with brisk nurses who wear " college trained" badges and demand high wages. They refer to "my charges," think only in terms of vitamins, and talk shallowly of psychology when "the charges" are a little difficult, because they are torn to shreds with homesickness for father and mother. Some are lucky enough to have simple, comfortable nannies with warm hearts and cosy laps and deep wells of sympathetic understanding. Others have mothers who knit and shop and sit up half the night making two garments into one. But there are no fathers here. That's the tragedy.

Nothing matters so much to a child as having the right sort of father. Apart from the few men who are bored with children, and there are not many, fathers are more successful, naturally, with children than women are. Unhampered by the protective, apprehensive instinct common to all mothers, they are free to meet the child on equal ground.

"Come and saw wood with me." How marvellous! A saw! The seven-year-old boy is enchanted to cut wood. Mother is out, so he runs off coatless, in a bitter wind, wearing house shoes on the wet ground and wields the saw, under a big steady hand, with untold delight. Of course he has a cold for a week afterwards, but he has gained something precious; confidence in himself, the worthiness to be a companion to Dad.

Never, never will he forget that day when a lasting sense of manliness was born.

And now few homes boast of fathers. Mother, racked with anxiety, is painfully aware of her shortcomings over cricket and football. There is no male background for her boys to grow up against. And how they resent it. Father's society gave just that bigger world flavour that young boys must have and that girls need but little less. It tides them over the years until they are emotionally and socially free of both parents.

Mother, no matter how loved, how selfless, must fall, to a certain extent, into the rôle of universal provider. To see that clearly saves her both pain and disillusionment. But Father remains always a figure of romance and power. It is difficult to explain the necessity of his absence. Why isn't he here to play with me? Why, indeed?

However, the better-off children have got somebody to look after them, nurse, mother or governess. But the slum child has no one. He is utterly dependent on the kindness, the goodwill, the energy of the foster parents into whose home he has been thrust. Who would know, who would care if they beat him or starved him? But he has come from a community that says: " Here's another child; what a nuisance; let's leave it alone," into a place where people will say " Here's a child, let's do all we can for it."

Mother love is a nebulous sort of thing that we once thought flourished in every woman, a lovely, warming instinct that flowered and strengthened with a child's coming. But that illusion has been destroyed. These pathetic little bodies are living monuments to neglect, indifference and idleness. " It's not the mother's fault; they can't help it; they've no money, no time." That is asserted over and over again. And yet if one mother can find the ways and means to decency why can't another?

These mothers have got their chance, long awaited, and admittedly, delayed. But will they take it? They have been accommodated in luxury flats which within a week have become pigsties. Back to slumland is their cry. Already some clamour for their children to be sent home; others ignore them altogether, indifferent to their welfare. Who can help them, and how? What can the individual or the Government do if parental co-operation cannot be gained? There is talk of building a new London. Yet it is not " Walls but men (and women) who make a city."

Give them water, electric light, free education, doctoring, birth control clinics, milk, day nurseries, higher pay, shorter hours! They have all this, rightly, and more. But has it improved the mother's outlook, standards? It seems not. Yet they are not old, remnants of the ghastly sweated age, born before decent living was possible in their state of life, but women of twenty to thirty. Their children are not even house-trained. What have their schools taught them? It is difficult to see. Certainly not the simple rules of cleanliness. No one can deny that the elements of hygenic behaviour are of more value to the community than a knowledge of reading and writing.

Both are desirable. This corner of Cornwall is crammed to overflowing with young people learning not only how to behave in a civilised fashion, but also struggling to master the intricacies of Latin and mathematics which must be nearly as difficult.

There is an expensive boys' school in one hotel, another for girls nearby. They wear different clothes for all their activities and spend hours daily trying to hit a ball with bats and racquets. Their fat legs and red cheeks strike a painful contrast to the small shoeless youngsters outside the gates. But though they meet and pass here, on such unequal ground, they stand together at a mutual turning-point in their lives.

The day will soon come when these galumphing girls and boys will all go to State schools and their parents will no longer do without pudding and cigars and new hats to pay the large bills now thought necessary for education. Fathers won't sit in the counting-house counting out their money, wondering if there will be enough for Polly to finish in Lisbon or Madrid if London is not considered good enough. Oh, no! Polly will have been so excellently and cheaply taught in her State school that papa will be able to give her a round-the-world trip by air, and show her something older, lovelier, more worthwhile than anything she will find in European art galleries. The seas and mountains of the world, unchanged since time began, untouched by war. Then she will understand what her brothers died for. Let her see India. Then she will know what the Empire means.

And these small Londoners will no longer be at the mercy of ignorant, shiftless mothers, even when they go back, because a new way of living will have been put before them. They will come to appreciate order, decency, fresh air; they will respond to kindliness and just treatment. Nor will they readily forget the comfort and care which is given to them here. Having once glimpsed the Promised Land they will struggle on towards it, and, maybe, take their parents with them.

Meanwhile here's another job for the women of Pollyon. First the children must be housed, fed, and then, somehow, clothed.

The little mixed farms outside the town are overwhelmed with orders; fat boiling fowls for the daughters of the wealthy, lettuces, apples, potatoes for everyone. Penruff, the grocer's, is wedged full of anxious women armed with baskets full of ration books.

" Can we register here, please? Do you deliver to High Towers Hotel, now St. Alice's School?"

Even the tiniest shops are doing a thriving trade. Every tin of fruit and sardines is sold within a week. There is not a beach sandal, bathing cap nor toothbrush left. Presumably the smart schools and the majority of these Pollyon invaders brought their toothbrushes with them. But perhaps a thousand foster mothers went out on the same morning and purchased the few remaining ones for their little visitors? Be that as it may there's not one to be had.

The lack of the most unlikely commodities is put down to the presence of evacuees. It is difficult to see how any number of children could instantly lessen the supply of paper stabbers, blotting paper, nibs and typewriter ribbons.

" Yes, I've got two ribbons somewhere," rummaging under the counter, " can't find them." A dozen boxes fall over but the desired objects are not revealed.

" May I look?"

I am sometimes allowed behind Smith's counter, in Godalming, to find the just exactly right paper, which saves much pulling out and pushing back.

" The girl is out helping with the evacuees. I'm only in charge of the shop for two hours."

So after all the excuse is, indirectly, justified.

No matter how ragged their clothing, the little Londoners always seem to have a penny for the ice-cream man who drives over the firm sands at low tide. Children and soldiers pour out from every bay and inlet to meet him. The cart is white, with gay green-gold lettering and snowy-coated attendant. The incredibly fat pony, whose staple diet from his appearance must be Cornish cream, has the calm nature that invariably accompanies deeply covered ribs.

" I want to sit on him, lift me up," clamours Sue. Ready hands hoist her up on to the broad sun-warmed back so pleasant to her bare legs. The Lemon Lick spreads with delicious coolness towards her ears, down her chin. The evacuees begin to feel more at home now that they can buy something in what corresponds to the street. They are shy at entering a strange shop where penny customers receive scant attention. But Dan, the ice-cream man, caters for and welcomes small purchasers.

He, too, is plump and benign, being a large consumer of dairy produce. Perhaps that is why babies look so deliciously placid. If Mrs. Treloon could be persuaded to try a milk diet all the canteen helpers would benefit. Her staple food might well be acid drops.

But she has her troubles. Beryl, her eighteen-year-old daughter, has been seen on the sands with a " common private soldier." Beryl, the most carefully brought-up young lady in all Pollyon, and already destined by her mother to be the bride of a promising young Merchant Service officer, whose parents live, with discreet elegance, in a large modern bungalow all lounge and sun-blinds.

But girls care nothing for birds in the bush. What's the good of a boy who is always at sea? Here is a bird in the hand, one Bombardier Box, with a solid business in Birmingham and melting eyes.

But he is not an officer. Only a single stripe enlivens his coarse khaki blouse. Mrs. Treloon sees the Army sharply divided into two classes of sheep and goats. Officers and men. She does not know that boys from Eton and Oxford start in the ranks. Many of the militiamen she serves are the sons of clergymen, barristers and generals.

She smothers her disapproval of Bombardier Box by remarking with a sigh that all the world is upside down—there she is right.

A convent school has been evacuated to Pollyon. They move into an old house near the canteen which is practically a ruin. It possesses neither water, light nor blackout, having been shut for three years. " But it is cheap, and the air is glorious and we have little money," the Mother Superior explains with admirable good sense, so both nuns and pupils toil to clean the dirt-grimed rooms, unlike the rich schools who employ Germanish methods of approach when house-moving. They can afford a vanguard of charwomen to flatten out the spider's defences and clear the way for the advancing infantry. But poorer establishments must bear the full brunt of the attack unaided. However, it's a change from lessons and the sea is just below, waiting to wash their work-wearied bodies.

Mrs. Blunt, blessed with an insight into the feelings of her fellows says, understandingly:

" However can those poor dear nuns get themselves cleaned? They'll never go in the sea. You can't tread on the beach for soldiers. Let 'em have good hot baths here."

So good hot water from the Council taps can gush over the

bodies that no man, no woman, must see, while half-grown girls flounder in the Atlantic's delicious freshness.

That the establishment comes from country depths is obvious because the girls perform their toilet at the windows with complete unconcern. Though not for long. But while it lasts this interests the soldiers very much who stroll along to the canteen after supper. There is gesticulation, whistling, cat-calling to and from a red-haired maid who leans excitedly from an attic casement, indicating that she will soon be down. This by-play brings more heads to the windows until half the school is leaning out to see what is going on.

All the men in one place. All the women in another, and therefore mutually irresistible.

No inner light illumines the pink, well-washed faces of these nuns. They look a little hard, a little cold, a little sad.

They shepherd the girls down to bathe, and hover, anxiously, at the sea's edge, like gaunt blackbirds with flapping wings fluttering in the salty breeze, their colourless faces averted from Ginger Scot in his brief trunks and all the male and female nudity so happily and carelessly displayed. Do they think it absurd or wrong? Does a terrible hunger for life trouble their starved hearts? So many worldly avenues are locked against them.

The new batch of children are from the poorest London homes. It is easy to picture the mothers behind them. A few have good teeth, healthy bodies; their little garments are patched and darned with infinite patience and skill, shoes have been carefully repaired.

But the majority are ragged, filthy, pitiful in their deplorable state of neglect. Some wear flashy clothes above grimy bodies, poor bones and faulty teeth being the price of the bicycles that they bring with them.

Green peas, seen for the first time, are regarded with suspicion. "Wot are they? Sweets?" asks one child, fascinated by the little green balls upon his plate. But he does not like them—nor will he touch salad. Odd that so thin and pale a boy should be choosy over food. Bread and butter or bread and jam has obviously been his staple diet, but in a week he eats everything with hearty relish.

"We 'as bread and water for two days afore Dad's paid," he remarks cheerfully.

The W.V.S. headquarters above the canteen is besieged by the recipients of these further six hundred children, almost half of whom are bootless, shirtless. The majority have no change of clothes. Mrs. Blunt sees and hears all this and she picks up the telephone.

Mrs. Treloon, Mrs. Jolly, the minister's wife, all the pillars of Pollyon come running to her call. Several hundred children already here are still in dire need of clothes as well. The problem is both big and urgent. Scissors, patterns are hastily collected. Mrs. Treloon brings in a huge roll of gingham and flannel from her shop. The machine makes a pleasant hum, like a velvety bumblebee drunk with summer sunshine. Gradually little shirts, frocks, and shorts take shape. There is a pleasant smell of cotton material, a comfortable litter of threads on the bare floor, a happy indication of life and movement in the old house that stood empty for so long.

There is to be a bridge drive to raise funds for clothing the evacuees. Everyone has reached rock bottom in their cupboards. Mrs. Blunt and others have toiled for hours at sewing machines with unflagging diligence remaking old clothes, but still ragged shirts and torn frocks are seen everywhere. And many more children will arrive next week. Winter lies ahead. Coats and boots must be provided. Pitifully little comes from East London homes. Many hands in Pollyon are willing to sew, but rationed material greatly increases difficulties. These children have coupons and no cash. Many people have cash and no coupons. This problem is tackled and overcome. The required amount of wool and boots is reckoned up. The necessary sum must be raised. Will I help? Of course, gladly, but I scarcely know clubs from spades and have no urge to learn. No matter. Tea helpers are wanted and I am nimble enough now with crockery. So one golden afternoon, when the sea is an almighty tumbled glory of crystal spray and deep sapphire shadows, when cliff grass is swept into grey-green and silver ripples high above the honey-coloured sands, half Pollyon gathers in the Crescent lounge behind shut windows. Tables, chairs, cards, pencils, ashtrays have been collected from everywhere. Kind Miss Blossom has put flowers on the mantelpiece.

Tea is laid in an alcove. Mrs. Treloon sweeps up. A study

in plum. Turban, frock, bag, shoes, all exactly the shade of a ripe damson. She considers navy too obvious; black too dressy. Nothing is wanting except Piccadilly as a background. Mrs. Blunt wears figured crêpe of grey and mauve with an historic waistline. The lawyer's wife a staggering tweed of bright red, while Miss Jolly, with admirable restraint, comes in pale blue linen which answers her eyes and sets off her naturally pink cheeks to perfection. Trim flannel suits, cotton frocks, and the black crêpe-de-chine of old age mingle in the doorway.

Poor little Mr. Friske plunges into the female swamp with an air of extreme dejection. He likes bridge with men only, or with women who don't chatter. He would prefer to give a guinea for wool rather than spend four hours in this glassed-in tank with fifty-nine women at the cost so much per head.

But his wife was adamant. What Would People Think if he did not support her in public? If they had no children, couldn't they help other peoples? At thirty she had shirked the responsibility of a family. From the dull safety-point of fifty she gibes her husband for their lack of olive branches.

Cards are shuffled; dealt; played. The atmosphere grows thick with smoke and breath. Two hours drag by. We set out milk-jugs, sandwiches, cakes, lemonade, then chairs are pushed back and the buffet is besieged. Someone suggests that fresh air would be welcome so a window is flung wide. In rushes the rumbustious Atlantic air, curtains fly out, horizontally, scattering cards and ashtrays, imperilling cups, threatening piles of buns, making the whole gathering seem puny and unimportant beside its magnificent strength.

Refreshment costs are included in the bridge tickets, so we do not have to fumble for change with one hand and pour out with the other. These women can drink almost boiling tea. After one sip, lo, it is gone. Quite different from the canteen where the soldiers prefer to let it cool. Perhaps more women wear dentures which serve as armour plating against heat. Food vanishes rapidly. Teapots grow empty.

Madam strolls in, very much the hotel proprietress, bowing, smiling, shaking hands like a well-trained child. No colour seems to have been left out of her get-up. Fancy jewellery embellishes her neck, ears, fingers, wrists. She has forgotten nothing, except

a nose ring.   At last the fifty-nine women and one man are fed.
He makes a gallant effort to wait on the ladies, but they are numer-
ically superior.   He is forced to retreat in the face of overwhelming
odds.   Lips are wiped, crumbs brushed from dresses, and stamped
cheerfully into the carpet.   Younger women peep into pocket
mirrors to renew their faces; older ones are past caring if their
hair is untidy or if their nose shines.   They were smart and pretty
in the last war.   Now they are tired with the dull hopeless fatigue
that comes after a lifetime of unalleviated domesticity.   They
have had no time to be interested in outside things.   Books, music,
travel, love affairs, all the blinding beauty and wonder of the
outside world has passed them by.   They have been smothered
by the mass of petty details that come from a ringed-in life.   Part
of them is happy, content with husband, home, children, and part
of them yearns, wistfully, for all the loveliness that they have
missed.

The bridge tournament produces a goodly sum.   Wool and
warm flannel is purchased: once again Mrs Blunt gets out the
sewing machine and we cast on for eight hundred pairs of legs.
Mrs. Blunt's two little evacuees are orphans now.   Their policeman father was killed trying to rescue hospital patients from
German bombs; their mother was burnt to death a week later.   So
no parcels come for them any more.

Mrs. Blunt, a woman of few words and slow emotions, sews
faster than ever and says, " We can give them a home for always.
That's a comfort."   They are too young for grief.   That, too, is
a blessing.   Was their mother, trapped behind flames, tortured
for their future, or dimly thankful, through her agony, of their
comparative safety?

We make the quaintest little socks of all the blue, khaki, red,
green and yellow oddments left over from children's jumpers.
But they are gay and warm.   Wool is hard to come by now, and
there is satisfaction in using every strand.   Bodies that were once
loved, warmed, well fed, protected, are now cold, numb with
the awful cold that destitution brings.   Homes gone, fathers gone,
mothers gone, and somewhere over forty thousand British prisoners
are locked up, at the mercy of their swinish captors.

Shoes are the worst problem.   It is possible to make little
garments from grown up cast-offs: to conjure knitted jerseys out

of unravelled pullovers, but no amateur, however ingenious, can make shoes out of nothing at all. Tattered soles that might hold together on smooth London pavements fall to pieces immediately on the rough cliff paths and cobbled harbour quay. But by degrees, as the want becomes widely known, people stroll in with gifts. Mrs. Blunt's garden shoes fit a boy of eleven to perfection. She misses them, but what of that? His need is greater. Her blue and red crêpe-de-chine, that has graced Pollyon's bridge evenings for three seasons, is now spread out dramatically, her scissors hover, uncertainly, before the major operation begins. Snick, snick, steel rips through silk, what a good thing there is a deep hem, two best frocks can be conjured out of this for some little person.

The workers clamber down the steep stairs and drink tea, thankfully, in the canteen kitchen. We are glad of their pennies.

" Sit right theer. Two teas, please."

Ginger Scot stretches his huge body, picks up the newspaper. A tiny boy is with him, in tattered clothes, with tear-stained face. He perches, nervously, on a chair, opposite the soldier, his little legs swinging above the floor.

" He wus crying, so I brrought 'im in." There is a note of apology in the deep, rough voice.

" He is not happy heer; he wants to go hoam to London."

" So do lots of us," says Alf, the Cockney, collecting a plate full of buns, which he puts before the child, and a cup of strong tea. Ginger pays.

Questioned, he tells the pathetic story. He is one of eight. His brothers and sisters left London some weeks ago. Mother has kept the new baby with her. He is here alone. He has never been alone, in a house without children, for ten minutes in his life.

His plate empties. Alf, noticing it, asks, " 'Nother tea, please." He pays this time.

" You and me both strangers 'ere, sonny," he grins. " My 'ome's in London; don't 'arf wish I was back."

Will they always miss the narrow bricked-in streets, the tarmac roads—so hot in summer, so cold in winter; the frowsty fruit stalls; fish and chip suppers under the flaming lights that now are dimmed? Will country peace ever bring balm to these street lovers? Alf and this boy have lived in a seething community of shared joys and sorrows; they yearn for the noise and smell of gutter life.

" Poor little chap. It's all wrong to have sent him to old Miss Green, who never even had a husband to look after." Mrs. Blunt puts down her cup, consults a ledger, and then goes out. She is just the woman to put the crooked straight. She comes back, smiling. All is arranged. Some motherly soul with two children of her own finds room for another. A tactful note is sent to the trim little spinster who can't understand small homesick boys.

" We've got a new home for you to-night, with other boys and girls. Will you like that?"

The boy eats stolidly, his mind misted with the horrors of the clean-sheeted bed, where he lay terrified by the silences of the neat room. The sun had streamed in and he wanted to be with the others playing on those wonderful sands, dipping his feet into the fresh pools, running races. At home he never went to bed till dark. Three others shared his mattress on the floor, and all the cheerful noise of living surged about him, the rich smell of frying, beer and pipe smoke, the coarse laughter, shrill voices of slumland had coloured his nights and days.

He eyes the kindly face above him with the tragic distrust of his breed.

" Neow. I wanter go 'ome."

Alf shoves a doughnut on his plate.

" Will you come with me when you have had your tea?" Mrs. Blunt smiles encouragingly.

" Neow, I wanter go with the soldier."

" Righto, come along a me," says Alf, not laughing for once. " Where do we go?"

Mrs. Blunt writes out an address. Man and boy, strange victims of circumstance, pass out together into the sunlight.

Evacuation brings every sort of difficulty in its train. There may be a momentary feeling of revulsion against the unfortunate little mites who bring additional dirt and disorder into homes where women are already exhausted with fighting against both these twin devils. But it melts instantly into the sun of sympathy, and the urge to help. Someone, somewhere, will care for a child that is in need. A hand is stretched out for him to grasp.

The well-off evacuees, and there are many, fall into a totally different category. Miss Mary Jolly, ejected by the Government from her Bristol abode, is not in the same plight as the city child. She has several alternatives. He has none and is hurled into a temporary home, unasked. She comes voluntarily to Farmer Jolly, who, by some extraordinary freak of fate, happens to be her brother.

She hates his farm. He has put his all into it, labour, cash, and just that something else which is much greater than either. But she's too stupid to understand that. Her mind still runs on a peace-time basis. No woman over thirty, who is not doing manual work (she, Mary, is over fifty and makes small use of both her brain and body), should eat bacon or cooked breakfast every day. That's bygone luxury. Bacon should be eaten for lunch or dinner. Not until the ink is dry upon the Peace Treaty should leisured women munch bacon breakfasts. Leave it to the workers who plough and make and man our guns. Her mentality, as well as her appetite, needs an overhaul.

And if she must keep a Pekinese (why not something British made?) can't she train it to eat cabbages instead of the soup bones upon which sensible families largely and healthily subsist?

Perhaps we are all trying when we live in other people's houses. It's as well to have a drastic callover of our failings when those of others become almost unbearable.

Do we use some meaningless expression with maddening persistence? "Quite so." "Very possibly." Do our dentures click when we eat toast? Is our soup disposed of with absolute silence? Is there a halo of crumbs about our chair after every meal? Do we, habitually, leave doors open, to bang in their own time? Is our outlook paltry and dull? Can we efface ourselves, unfailingly, for a period each day, during our sojourn under another's roof?

If not, we can't criticise Farmer Jolly's sister.

All over Britain women are doubling up because their husbands are fighting and shillings are scarce; or their homes may be tragic heaps of rubble. Aunts, cousins and in-laws crowd together in slum-like proximity. Maids flee before the advancing hordes, who arrive at a moment's notice for an indefinite period. In humble homes, where meals are eaten in the kitchen, and girls cheerfully share double beds as a matter of course, the situation lacks the tautness that grows in richer establishments. There is no choice on either side. It must be, and is, done. But it is difficult for all concerned. Soldiers, sailors, monks, convicts, boys, girls, can apparently live happily together with the minimum of privacy. But grown women, No. It is not easy for a country-woman with several young children to share her kitchen with her Bristol-evacuated town-bred, London, or Portsmouth equivalent. And it must be equally awkward for Mary Jolly, wedded to bridge, pavement life and a 1912 outlook to " muck in" with farming relations, who work, as farmers do, while Mary chats. The whole scheme of living in thousands of homes has been changed with bewildering suddenness from a quiet stream into a tempestuous whirlpool.

Houses that seemed small a few years ago have suddenly become too large. Not too big for the owner's tastes and comfort. But not small enough for his purse. So others must come to live in it. A great sacrifice. However, only meals are shared. Nothing else. People with half their lives behind them have earned the right to privacy when they want it. Busy tenants with fully occupied days are obviously the most desirable. Then the arrangement suits all concerned, since no one's liberty is threatened. Life in two or three rooms is very much the same as it always was in wider spheres.

But the sifting process is slow, and sometimes painful, as it is when searching for wives, husbands, cooks or lovers. The highest references demanded and given may only reveal that somebody's father was a bishop. Or he may have commanded a brigade or battle-cruiser with conspicuous success.

But of what use is that if he is half an hour late for every meal, thereby throwing all the domestic machinery out of gear? And none of the burning questions can well be asked, such as " Are you reasonably tidy? Do you pay your bills? Are you good-tempered?"

Of course such queries are not put when embarking upon emotional adventures or when engaging a secretary. But in neither case do they signify with equal force. Love overlooks all, and secretaries can be steadily dismissed until the right one is found.

Some pursue these tactics in marriage, but the exhaustion and expense incurred acts as a general deterrent.

So the very utmost caution is needful at the outset of negotiations.

Of course the prospective visitors may hurl a bombardment of questions about their possible change of base. They really have every right to. After all, you know what to expect at the Ritz, or the Metropole, Brighton. But a private house is different. They may demand, "Is the cooking good? Are there lumps in the porridge—or in the bed?"

Treat the matter lightly. Laugh, say "Come and see." A bed can be tried out any time of the day. Not night; it is full then. But it might be difficult to produce specimen porridge on a hot summer afternoon. The transaction seems reminiscent of the Three Bears, who were so tiresomely exacting about beds and porridge.

But such matters are trivial. Petty irritations pale before the problem of the bombed-out or evacuated child. He must be housed, washed and fed, however great the difficulties may be. And more. Little enough love and care has ever come his way. Can't he have some now?

Every mother who tucks up her own children feels that stirring in her heart. Because at any moment she, and they, may be in the same position. How should we like to think of our boys and girls being pitchforked into different and possibly hostile surroundings, two, three hundred miles away? It is sad enough to hear a child ask for the daddy who does not come. What will he feel without his mother as well?

It's agony to think that Sally and Sue, always sure of a welcome, might look up into a cold, hard face, and realise for the first time, with bitter surprise, that they are not wanted, waking, in that harsh moment, to the full knowledge of life's cruelties. Their little laughter-lit faces plead for those others, so puny and perplexed, with a forcefulness greater than words.

Chapter VI

THE CANTEEN

THE PIE-DISH FULL OF MONEY HAS GONE. MR. TRELOON HAS presented the canteen with a till. A grand hideous contraption. The mother must have been a tank and the father a typewriter. It looks thoroughly unwholesome and has a mulish nature.

Nobody except Mrs. Treloon can get an answer out of it. She was brought up on tills, so now, naturally, avoids them. It is embellished with enough nobs for a submarine or the B.B.C. organ. Mrs. Blunt spent half an hour mastering its intricacies, pushing, pulling, probing to gain speed and confidence. Coins jump about quite out of control, appearing, disappearing with the unexpectedness of rabbits from a conjuror's hat. Here is a shilling. In it goes. Bang! Ting! Ting! Slam! How is the change obtained? Push this. Phut! Sixpence is flung into the air. Don't want that. Try this nob. Gr . . . rr . . . r. Silence. It has become wedged. After much coaxing the new treasure leaps to life again. But it is several days before we dare use it in business hours. The cash is uncontrolled enough already without the additional complication of this armoured affair.

When it was possible to keep a pad beside the pie-dish and write down, in haste and secrecy 2s. 6d.

1s. 9d.

9d. there was the answer.

Figures cannot lie. But this mechanisation of money confuses us all. The thing has brought a taint of commerce into our canteen; but financial stability is essential; the pie-dish overflowed with cash, and no business can afford to " get stuck fast in yesterday."

All sorts of changes are needed to meet increasing trade.

We are gradually becoming mechanised, having acquired a till, a, so-far dumb, wireless, and the promise of a piano. Some magician has renewed the innards of the gas cooker. Now the oven, once a lukewarm, rusted cavern, emits furious heat, and an additional gas ring has been put in, that makes a circle of spiky blue-gold flames, like the haloes of saints in old-time story-books.

This will enable us to do hot suppers. Soup. Sardine toast, Welsh rarebit, eggs in different guises. The extreme smallness of kitchen and scullery will make the preparation of even simple dishes difficult, but we shall learn to manage.

" Chips, can we have chips?"

It's hateful to say " No," but where to find the fat in sufficient quantity? In these strange days when there is no fresh blotting-paper in the banks, when people thankfully eat the sort of cheese with which they formerly only baited their mouse-traps, when boot repairs take three weeks and every hairpin has died, lumps of fat have become treasures beyond price. It may be only a matter of time before the barter system reigns. That will relegate money to the place where it belongs.

How much more satisfactory to exchange a sofa, which was never really right in the smoking-room, for a second-hand school outfit for Sue; to dispose of the handsomely bound, but never read, classics for a cucumber frame, while an eiderdown and winter overcoat might well pass from one owner to another with mutual advantage.

As the whole world grows poorer drawing-rooms may become

caravan-serais of business, where, in return for light refreshments, all comers can strike a happy bargain with each other.

Meanwhile the searchlight falls on fat. Every ounce must do the work of two, three. No bone must be left unturned to find this precious commodity which has shrunk almost to vanishing point.

Mrs. Treloon, for all her worldliness, equals Mrs. Blunt in her knowledge of the domestic arts. There is nothing that either of them do not know about food. Their methods are different from mine. I beseech the butcher. They browbeat him, which proves more successful since they obtain a few ounces of suet to " run down." This process is not known as " melted," but the results are identical. With the fat thus procured they make Cornish pasties of airy lightness. What to put in them? Not sausages, which would fit in as neatly as tube trains into their tunnels, but savoury substitutes which are nearly as good.

Chopped egg and ham (Mr. Jolly's pig obliges with the ham), scraps of sardine, tomato, onion, potato. They produce jam tarts for two a penny; fruit flan in twopenny slices. The ingredients are given by both these women, and they cook Saturday-night " extras" of this sort in their own homes. They have shown us how to make a purée of melted margarine (with a little milk), sardines, tomato juice and mayonnaise sauce which is made into sandwiches while the margarine is still warm. The easiest, quickest, most economical way.

In the brave new world, which won't be a quarter as brave as this war-time one, people will no longer ask, " Is your boy going to Eton?" Instead the question will be, " Do you run down your fat?" There'll be no money left to pay for even unrationed margarine.

If the making of refreshments is difficult the fair disposal of them is even more so. How to divide thirty-six pasties between sixty men? Small ones, at a penny-halfpenny each, now take the place of the larger threepennies, but even so the problem bristles with complications. If six pasties are on the counter when ten men come in, who is to prevent one man from eating three? Nobody. Is it wiser to serve fifteen customers with a pasty each on a slack afternoon, or put out fifty and let a hundred men take their chance of getting one? Which is the most disappointing, actually to see your pal swallow the remaining tit-bit or to arrive and be told that there are no pasties? Even if we sold them only between stated hours they wouldn't go round, and it's pasties the men want, above all else.

But a little Cornish canteen, full to bursting of British soldiers, with only coppers to spend, can't be run on the lines of an Overseas Club. There food is procurable in almost fantastic quantities. Great pans of bubbling fat. Turkeys. Chickens. Chocolate cakes. Where do the turkeys come from?

It is questionable if even soldiers need soup, roast turkey, two veg. and all the cakes that they can eat as " snacks" between their ample rations. But I have helped to serve such meals to our magnificent Dominion men at 3.30 on a hot May afternoon. Their appetites must be seen to be believed. Yet their bodies remain slim, incredibly strong. No superfluous ounce thickens their iron and whipcord limbs or mars their clear-cut faces. And their teeth would earn them a living in the advertisement world. Perhaps the best teeth, like the best people, thrive on hard work.

Why do our brothers from overseas eat double the amount of the British Army? Is it because they are richer, or more virile? Do the children of a new country need more than the sons of an old Mother? Perhaps if we all ate as they did we might gain something of their physical splendour. We have been told for years that we all eat too much; that we should still feel hungry when a meal is completed. Perhaps the doctors and the dietitians have been fooling us all the time, and we don't eat half enough.

If double helpings will turn us into lions of courage and endurance and unfailing cheerfulness like our Dominion men, let's learn from the young lands, and treble our intake when ration books can be thrown in the fire.

But Spike, Ginger Scot, and even the little Cockney Alf, are just as fit in a different way, as the overseas troops. Not so large, not so handsome, but their sticking power, their ability to endure incredible fatigue is just as great. It is a miracle that it should be so. How can Alf, Hoxton born and bred, face up to the rigours of war as does his prairie-worker equivalent? And yet he does. He is short: spotty: ill-fed until he joined the Army. His nights have been spent in a fetid room, damp, foul-smelling from bad air, lack of ventilation; his days in a filthy little shop. No playground but a street. No love, no care, no thought, nothing that makes for growth has ever been given to him. Light, air, food, the rights of every man have been denied him, and yet now his poor body responds to healthy living so that he can fight and march and toil alongside those men from the great wide sunny countries where children under open skies strengthen and ripen easily as apricots on a warm wall.

Spike was brought up on potatoes, and Ginger Scot, very likely, on whisky in a Glasgow slum. Like Alf, they've never had the right vitamins, warm clothes, thick boots, games, sunshine. And yet their toughness is legendary.

Perhaps toughness isn't really a physical thing, but something much deeper. Whatever it may be, the British have it in a way that no other nation has. No matter if they come from South Africa—Canada—Cornwall—Australia—New Zealand—London— it's the same blood, new stock or old—the same. The French aren't tough and not fundamentally cheerful. Disasters quickly destroy their superficial gaiety. They laugh when life goes right but their rallying power is small. The only true stickers are the British. Soft living may break them, but hardships never. Cut their cash—cut their food—double their work, and they thrive on it.

"Why are women so much nicer than they used to be?" asks the Duchess, meditatively. "I believe it's because they eat less. It's difficult now for even the most self-indulgent dowager to upset her liver, and the poor could never afford to." For generations many women never "worked off" their food; it just clogged their brains and exhausted their bodies. So at forty they were finished. In proportion to their size and physical output they have generally eaten more than men. And now they don't even eat their full rations. All of them give bits of their sugar and meat and bacon to their husbands and children. Once-stout women have now become just attractively plump; slim women have shrunk into the thin category, while thin women are mere bags of bones kept going by the flame inside them.

Daisy, on the other hand, has never eaten so much. She is distended with buns. Perhaps that is why her temper is short, and the Duchess is right about female overeating.

"Tea, please! Tea, please!" Daisy has mastered the new words at last. So she was listening after all when she sat motionless before Spike while he repeated the formula. What a pity she did not reward him for his patience and greet him one Friday evening with the hard-won phrase instead of giving tongue to it one Monday afternoon at three o'clock with only me to hear it.

There is a special quality about first things that dies with repetition.

Will she say it again for him on Friday, or will she look at him wordlessly for many weeks, and then demand "Tea, please!" when Spike has gone in the sudden way that soldiers move from county to county, continent to continent.

It is her unexpectedness that has endeared her to him. Perhaps that is why parrots appeal more to men than to women. Like the female sex they invariably say and do exactly what is not expected of them. A refreshing quality.

Sometimes Spike takes her out of the cage, opens the door, holds out a finger, and Daisy, with all the deliberation of an old lady leaving a taxicab, steps on to it. She is very clumsy on her feet, and once off the perch moves like a rheumatic charwoman. It is tragic to see her caution, little feeble legs and inability to use her freedom. There is something awful about bars that hem a living creature in.

Gradually she gains confidence and balance. Forsaking Spike's finger she clambers up his rough sleeve which offers firmer foothold, and finally gains his shoulder. From this vantage point she surveys the world, making crooning sounds of pleasure. Another move brings her to the red lobe of Spike's ear. She regards this phenomenon intently for several minutes, fascinated, immobile. Then begins caressing it with her murderous beak. Spike might have had his ears nibbled by parrots daily since birth, so calmly did he accept her quaint attentions.

Sergeant Sly, the canteen Adonis, limps in and throws a contemptuous smile at Spike and Daisy. Sly is in hospital recovering from severe leg wounds. He is one of those men born to drive women crazy. Wavy red hair springs away from his beautifully shaped head, set so well upon his shoulders. Very little matters about a man except his head and shoulders. If they are right, he's right all over.

But Sly has everything else as well: splendid limbs; straight features; navy-blue eyes, dark as damsons beneath his coppery curls, dangerous, compelling eyes. We all look up when he comes in, even Mrs. Blunt and the Duchess, with her calm face, and women who aren't young any longer.

Such men should not walk about loose, but Sly's is not a wholesome allure, like Gary Cooper's. It's frightening. He'd make a million in Hollywood. As my old Aunt said, " Gary Cooper's charm must be terrific for me to feel it at seventy-five."

Sly is not a regular visitor. It's a long walk from the hospital, and lines of pain darken his face as he drags his unwilling leg along. What is his history? Impossible to guess. Life with him would be like reading the Sunday papers, all sparks and flames and adventures mixed with deep despairs and bitter doubting agonies. Life with Spike would be like reading *The Times*, a sober mid-level experience, without excitement, but comforting, reliable.

Unlike most soldiers Sly is impossible to read, difficult to place. He fences himself round with hard, bright conversation, impenetrable as a wall of steel. Perhaps he is afraid of being questioned about things he is striving to forget. Perhaps the writhing horrors in his mind won't die and he is terrified that some stupid woman will try and revive them by her senseless chatter. But by degrees even Sly begins to thaw. A friendly face, a friendly manner, and above all, the sense of being welcomed and understood dispels any doubts these men may have about us.

They can come in and be left entirely alone, if it's solitude they crave for, or they can talk about their wives, mothers, and new as-yet-not-seen baby and be sure of interested listeners. Sly is always polite and yet there is a hint of contempt in his manner towards the canteen establishment. He looks as if he expected carpeted floors, waitresses with two feet of skirt and beribboned hair, and he finds only bare boards and other men's wives and a few women who are hardly women at all. Sly is the sort of man who is found dead in a flat with a stocking round his neck. And every woman would understand why.

But he has his uses. The day the piano arrived he was invaluable. Madam, of the Crescent Hotel, has an ancient upright Broadwood " by her," i.e. tucked away in a passage to make room for the full-sized grand that sprawls about the lounge like a spreading chestnut tree: not a thing of beauty until the right person brings it to life.

Would she lend the disused one to the soldiers? Of course, of course, take it by all means. Thank you very much. But how? A luggage barrow, with small tight wheels, and a contrary steering handle is procured. But who is to push it up the hill for nearly a mile to the canteen? There is no one capable of lifting weights in the hotel except the chef, and he is far too grand, being deeply embedded in that's-not-my-work attitude. The "boots" is a frail old man high up in the seventies.

Oh, for a lusty male in this wilderness of women! But the housemaid, who wears merely an overall, sandals and a wedding-ring, has boy friends. Scores of them, both in the Services and in the C.3 ranks. The rickety newspaper man exists only for her smiles, and "she'd love to help the soldiers." We are not concerned with the wages of indiscretion—all we want is a piano. So her admirers lay ready hands on the faded mahogany relic and appear willing to trundle it all over Cornwall if it means gaining her favours. We find it waiting in the gutter outside the locked canteen at two o'clock. Good, there'll be men in plenty here to carry it in.

An hour passes. No customers. Rain starts to fall. Two mackintoshes are draped over the abandoned instrument, the arms tied together like drunken puppets. Then Sly limps in, hoping to make the wireless work. If he can do that he deserves to be made Commander-in-Chief of all the Mechanics in the Army.

Nailed boots in the passage at last. Spike. He clumps in, asks of Sly: "Wot's that set out in the street?"

"Piano; give us a hand. We'll bring it in."

"But . . ." Impossible to remind him of his lame leg. That would anger him. They can't do it between them with Sly half a cripple. They'll drop it. On the other hand, they won't want women all mixed up with their arms and the piano's legs. Embarrassment must not be added to existing difficulties. It's not far; only into the little room by the door. Perhaps they'll manage.

Thump! Down comes the Broadwood on to the pavement with a twanging shudder.

"Now then, in with it."

Sly's long capable hands and Spike's broad ones take the strain and a moment later the piano stands opposite the green velvet sofa, giving an added touch of homeliness to the room. Spike leans over the top of it, waiting for the flicker of pain in the other's face to die away as he straightens the wounded leg.

"Kin you play it?"

"Yes, I can," is the unexpected reply.

Sly runs his fingers over the keys with the ease and skill of long use. The hardness in his face melts away. Release has come to him with this new-found toy. Sly, whose cold manner and bitter tongue, once repelled his fellows, is now a magnet to whom all are drawn. He comes in nearly every day, and when he is not there the others ask: "Where's the chap who plays the piano?"

Sometimes they gather about him and sing, songs that have become almost hallowed because of their association. Who can ever hear "Waltzing Matilda" without seeing Australians marching, marching over dust and stones, through sand and sun. . . .

> Up rode the squatter mounted on his thoroughbred
> Up rode the troopers, one, two and three . . .

The beat of their feet, the beat of their hearts, all the pride and love and tears of the Commonwealth throbs through the melody . . . "You'll never take me alive said he." . . .

Do Germans sing as they march and fight? It seems not. Ask a dozen British soldiers, and they'll all say the same. No song born from the spontaneous joy of living as free men ever comes from the dull, coarse lips of those downtrodden puppets, pummelled into sullen submission by their bullying leaders.

Fear, threatened and applied, hangs over every German soldier; he is beaten, starved, tortured for the smallest offence in peace or war. Look at his face. Dull, hopeless, wooden, all the light that comes of little everyday joys has been stamped out of him by iron-shod German heels. He is furtive, frightened, fettered, a trained toy, jerked hither and thither by military maniacs for their own gain. They don't care if his boots and body are broken; let him march till he drops; leave him to die where he falls. What's a German soldier? Just nothing at all.

But whether or not they sing this is certain. They don't laugh and they can't write music like "Waltzing Matilda" that twists your heart and fills your eyes. Anyone who has seen German troops goose-stepping along, in films or in reality, will exclaim, "Here are men who cannot smile."

Watch the newsreel. " This is the British Army on manœuvres . . ." Or see them in the flesh thumping along the King's highway. Laughter ripples up and down their ranks. They whistle, sing, and there is music in their feet. Yes, music in those rough Army boots so stiff and hideous in themselves, so magical when mustered in scores, hundreds, thousands—the feet that have freed the world.

Not the German sort of music that fills concert halls with long-haired men and short-haired women, who can't even sing God Save the King, much less play it. But something infinitely finer. The cheerful noise of a free and happy people.

The Ploughshire Colonel came in to-day, young in years, but grey-haired with old eyes. He brought half his battalion back from France, and all his youth died with those he left behind. He talks to us in the way that soldiers do, without stiffness. Here is a man whom nothing could surprise, dismay, intimidate.

We have often heard of a barrack inspection. Now, perhaps, we are to be submitted to one. Will he come into the kitchen and peer into the battered saucepans, or is it just a thank you visit on behalf of the men? He questions the Duchess with interested thoroughness. Do we pay our way? Have we enough helpers? Are the premises easy to run? Can we obtain such foodstuffs as we require? The canteen is greatly appreciated by the men. May he see it all?

The vast coal range attracts him. " Heavens! you don't have to cook on that?"

" No, gas; here, in the scullery."

" Where do you all go in a raid?"

" Stay here. There hasn't been a bad one yet."

He sifts and places us instantly, as men who know the world do, asking the Duchess about accounts, Mrs. Treloon about the feeding, with unerring insight into the workings of our establishment.

Sly, unaware of distinguished company, is singing in the little room, " Does she love me, yes or no?" The Colonel hears and wonders—— Ah! Does she?

" Yes! Yes!" shouts Daisy in a frenzy of delight at such an illustrious visitor.

That's a good omen!

He laughs; the strategy of indirect approach is not in him. He goes to her with the straightness which is the only way to her heart, holds out a finger, ribbons for bravery are upon his chest, while she flirts and bobs and curtseys in his honour.

" Tea, please! Tea, please!"

All her best phrases are being trotted out.

" She talks well."

" Spike taught her."

He looks up, surprised.

" He's my servant."

" We both come from Oxfordshire, so we are friends."

" A grand fellow, Spike."

He clatters up the stairs, looks at the writing-room, with its dart-board, magazines and flowers on the mantelpiece.

" Excellent, all of it. Exactly what's needed. I am very grateful; so are the men, but they can't say so."

He smiles, and passes out into the steep street mellowed by the afternoon light. Girls go up and down, on foot, or bicycling in pale summer frocks. Most of them have soldier escorts. They look cheerful, carefree. The little shops are clean and gay. Rosy, well-fed children tumble about the pavements.

He faces the four-mile walk to camp feeling unaccountably lonely, and suddenly aware of a revulsion against men. Day after day, month after month, year after year, only men about him. Fighting, training, marching, and at night, male gossip, coarse male jokes, rough weather-beaten faces everywhere. Bare floors; black iron beds; cotton sheets and Army blankets. Tin basins to wash in. A sixpenny shaving mirror. Some girl had given him a grand silvery one, once, because she was rich, and hoped to marry him, but he didn't like her and the mirror was broken now.

He is sick of sixpenny shaving mirrors and cheap ugliness of war-time. Barrack life is the best in the world when you are young, and again, after and during marriage, so husbands told him. But marriage is only an episode to men. An essential background, but a background, always. No more.

And in between there comes a fleeting moment when barrack life is hell and that moment has come upon the Colonel here and now. Frantic, desperate week-end affairs in London had cured his old-time restlessness temporarily before the war. But they wouldn't do any longer. He wanted something quite different.

Someone, some place to come back to. He'd never had a home to remember. Just a father in China; a mother who had often to be abroad; aunts in the holidays. There was not one room in his mind that he could look back on and call his home. No settled place in which he had battled through all the jungle of emotions that beset his youth.

And, somehow, the sight of our bare stone house, converted into some sort of temporary home for the soldiers roused in him a surging desire for a place that he could call home. Everything about the canteen is makeshift, the crockery is odd, the tables rickety, chairs hard. Crumbs, slopped tea; crumpled papers and a group of little-town women in a sun-splashed scullery hung with teacloths, banners of their calling.

Yet there is more kindly warmth there than in the hideous quarter where he would drink his tea, alone.

Soldiers ought not to marry. Even in peace they had work to do that women could not share. You can't take a woman to Gilgit, the Khyber, and even at the Staff College they are in the way. It's much easier to " get on" without a wife. A married adjutant is frowned upon; Generals like dealing with bachelor Colonels, who don't want to sneak off and see their sons play cricket for their school.

Attractive wives are dangerous, because soldier husbands have to leave them alone so often, and dull ones are a deadly bore. He'd heard it all thrashed out a thousand times in the past when such things mattered. But now it was all different because anyone's life might end to-day, to-morrow. Half his regiment had been killed in one afternoon. And did he want to get on? Not if it meant long spells at Aldershot or the War Office. Emphatically not. He couldn't stand hearty women who played golf as well as he did and rode much better. But women weren't doing such things now. Perhaps they never would again in the same way. There might be diminished leisure in the coming years and it's much easier to live with a woman who works than just a good-time girl. He didn't really like women; he didn't understand them. But he loved one.

Of course love has to be kept in its proper place, like boots and pipes and shirts. Fatal to let it get mixed up with the business of soldiering. But marriage means more than just having a woman in your life; it is all intermingled with the atmosphere of charming flower-filled rooms, books, a feeling of peace. A sort of coming home. Opening your own front door (a Government front door, but, nevertheless, sacred to each successive " owner"), going into a bedroom that looks like a sitting-room instead of a monk's cell; scented soap; fine towels to wipe away sweat and grime and tiredness. Not the coarse, bright, striped affairs that soldier servants buy for bachelor officers. And having somebody who really cares when marching orders come. All that counts for so much.

It's hell to leave a wife behind on the platform, thinking " Thank Heaven she's got the sense not to wait about and wave" when your own throat feels like a barrage balloon, and your baggage, labelled for the far end of the world, is being hoisted on to the rack.

But it's worse to have no wife to leave.

Yet the process of acquiring one is both a difficult and delicate matter, because the vital questions are seldom, if ever, asked, and then comes the bitter experience of seeing imagined perfection rotted by disillusionment. To a woman, marrying the life she likes matters as much if not more than the man she likes, because he will be out from nine till six. But his manner of living must become hers. If she wants to give a greater part of each day to social service, painting, music, or business let her say so beforehand " or else for ever after hold her peace." And if he means to smoke cigars in bed and have six shildren let him do likewise.

But ignorance has its advantages. Few women would take on a suitor with these known proclivities and she may come to agree with him eventually.

Perhaps the time is not far off when we shall advertise for marriage partners on the " Wanted—post-as-companion—sleep-alone" lines:

Major requires wife; must be early riser; good traveller; child lover. Highest references given and demanded.

Can she cook, or rather, will she? But a complete Martha must at all costs be avoided and a balance mixture is the very devil to find. The phrase " for hotter, for colder" might well be added to the Marriage Service for Army weddings, as any couple who have shared a home on the Equator or a tin hut during Catterick's winter will readily agree.   A wife who wilts when mercury registers 90 and upwards is useless to a man whose work lies in such places.

Brides should be able to question their possible mates without being thought peculiar.   Schools, who only have brief charge of our young, demand every possible question of the most private nature.

"Does your child suffer from any hereditary complaints?   Is she subject to fits *of any kind*—thus classing extravagance and epilepsy under a comprehensive heading.   Was her primary vaccination successful?"

If a young ladies' Seminary wants to know such things, surely any woman has the right to question her fiancé in like manner. But it would be awkward to greet him with " Do you suffer from liver attacks?"   " Are you a dope fiend?", when he arrived to take his lady love out to dine.

Proposing, like the canteen kitchen, wants cleaning up.

Spike is tidying his room when he goes in.   Its stark hideousness strikes him afresh.   The sun beats brazenly on the corrugated roof, and the windows, unadorned save for blackout shutters, look like a railway waiting-room. Spike clumps away. Clumps back bearing a tin tray.   The Colonel's tea.   He sets it down, very carefully, on the deal table.   Thick china.   A white enamel teapot. Chipped.   Four slices of bread and butter, one slice of cake.

If she says " Yes" they'd have silver tea-things, thin, old china, deep comfortable chairs, a thick carpet, and perhaps . . .

" Any letters for post, sir?"

" Yes, ready in half an hour," then, changing, " No, none to-night, thank you."

The tea is strong; he likes it weak but he is sweating from his walk and drinks it gratefully.   Then he pushes the tray aside, lights his pipe, takes out a pen, shakes it—never do to begin with blots—and writes, without hesitation:

" DEAREST,

Do you think you could ever care enough for me to marry me?   It would be too wonderful for words if you said ' Yes' but I shall quite understand if you say ' No.'

I shall understand because I have realised since I first met you that I have got out of step with the younger world—or perhaps it is that I have always been in step only as a soldier—not listening to other bands and other tunes. But if one keeps looking at the sky and not on the ground there's always hope, don't you think?

I think I could fall into a new step easily, quickly. I know I could with yours, for I know it so well. But it's asking a lot from somebody not quite young, to say may he come with you for a walk for life.

But there are wonderful things to be seen in our soldier life; other countries—other peoples, and it's sometimes damnably hot. There's good and bad—the extremes—but that's better any day than the dead-level course with neither mountain nor valley. I believe mine has actually been the dull, dead-level course—but I've only just realised it—bugles to wake one up, bugles to tell you to eat, bugles to send you to bed—and the same lot of fellows doing the same things at the same times—a first-class lot of fellows. Would you care to marry me and meet them?

I know it's sudden—this proposal—sudden for you, but I've never had any doubt in my mind from the first day I met you.

Ever yours

—— ——

Then he reads it once through, slips it into an envelope and walks to the post.

What would she say? "Yes?" "No?" "I'm not sure?" It's no fun to marry a soldier in war. But peace will come, with victory, and he may still be alive to enjoy it—with her. Then, perhaps, she may find that something in the Army which will want to make her stay there.

Not in the superficial part that only outsiders see, the bleak gaunt quarters of yellowish brick. Some contractor must have bought half the yellow brick in England about 1900 for married officers' houses. Not in the sherry parties, the race meetings, if they ever come back, the games, the dances and fun. But in all the flood of living that ebbs and flows about the barrack square. The pulses of a thousand young, vigorous bodies beat there. And to be one of them brings untold happiness to many women.

No band plays now upon the parade ground. But it will again. And bugles still blow.

Barrack life has a character all its own. There are soldiers everywhere—checking stores, carting coal, cleaning lorries. Vast numbers apparently doing nothing at all with engaging cheerfulness. That is the secret of the soldier's charm, perhaps. They have happiness to sell. Some look out of the windows, whistling, their hands polishing equipment. Others clean doorsteps that are already immaculate. A few, gloriously at ease, lie stretched upon their hard beds with every semblance of luxury, thinking what fools others are to work so hard.

Children, grubby maybe, but undoubtedly happy, tumble about the married quarters while their mothers rub up the fat brass elephants that they have collected in all those strange places where the British flag flies. There is a richness, a warmth, a great throbbing vitality about the crowded ever-moving life inside those bare red walls that look so much the same in Peshawar, Plymouth, Colchester, Cairo. Tall iron gates. A sentry outside. A guard-room within. Sometimes lilac blooms about the doorway and sometimes dusty rained-starved palms and sometimes only great sickening stretches of lifeless sand or miles of seething Eastern alleyways.

But no matter where they be, these men and women who have missed so many English springs carry their own laughter with them, and having once shared their journeyings, life in another setting is chilly, commonplace and colourless.

But will she guess all that? Or does she see the Army as a crazy sort of roundabout that gleams and glitters and beckons, a gaily painted, fascinating, quickly moving affair, with heartbreaks and tawdry values behind the tinsel? Does she see only the partings, the disappointments, the difficulties; and would she rather share a stockbroker's life in one settled place, far, far removed away from the ships, the seas, the lighthouses of the world? Of course she can see all that if she does marry a business man—see it in comfort, and in her own time, but only as a spectator. She could never be part of it, as the women are who follow the drum and who make a home wherever their husband's work carries them.

Perhaps she wouldn't care to live in an Indian bungalow clothed with Morning Glory and pale pink geraniums; perhaps she doesn't want to see a full moon rise over the Pacific or dawn break on the Roof of the World. Perhaps she does not even want the Colonel of the Ploughshire Regiment with all his men and guns and cars and files and endless journeyings.

He stares out over the sea, wondering.

It would be "cowdust" hour in India now. Cattle would be coming in to the Punjab villages and the cloud of dust they made would be turned to sheer gold in the short green twilight there, which is different from any other in the world. Men would be drifting home from polo, back to the club or to their women and all the cantonment would be disturbed by the scent of jasmine strengthening in the freshening night air.

India . . . India. . . . Did it still look the same . . . feel the same . . .? All the movement and magic and mystery of it. But nobody there was happy now, they were longing to get away, men and women alike. When Britain's in trouble it's hell to be out of it all.

He's due for leave in three weeks. Leave! Magical word conjuring up every facet of war-time life. There is a sort of leave look about the soldiers now. Ginger Scot is off to Glasgow, Spike to Woodstock and Alf to Hoxton. Preparations are being made in countless homes to receive Corporals and Captains, Brigadiers and Bombardiers.

In some cases the best linen sheets are being aired; the last bottle of sherry, saved for so long, is decanted; his favourite brand of cigarettes obtained with difficulty. In others the kitchen is scrubbed to welcome the warrior; an extra hundredweight of coal conjured out of the week's money, the spare pound of sugar, saved for a rainy day, is brought out for a sunny one. And every wife, both rich and poor, scrapes up little bits of butter, jam and cheese for the happy day when Master walks in.

Wives, with bodies aching from unaccustomed work in factory or home, make desperate efforts to appear gay and carefree for their husband's homecoming. A shampoo hastily done themselves, because a child can't be left, or the shops are all closed when their work is done, a frantic search in the mirror wondering will he notice all the new lines that sleepless nights have placed there. Some coffee, a couple of aspirins, a touch of lipstick, an absurd hat with bright feather to keep his eyes away from her tired face. There! She is ready. Soldier wives have always lived that way, even in peace. Complete uncertainty rules their lives. A hard training that makes life easier now. They have stood on quays and platforms so often watching ships and trains taking half their lives away. Have come down to breakfast in a just-settled house to find marching orders waiting in an envelope. Goodbye, England. But wives must be left behind.

It is infinitely harder for the civilian wife, with her ordered, unvarying days to face the shipwreck that war makes of family life. Her roots go straight down into one known place—her home. The soldier's wife, too, has roots that strike down wherever and whatever her home may be—roots that have to be constantly dragged up. Separation must be doubly hard to endure when it comes first in war without the peace-time experience that gives balance to it.

The Ploughshire Colonel walks home; slower than usual, his eyes on the sea that is now blue, now silver, now purple-shadowed green, slashed with gold and topped with snowy spray.

Cornwall. He won't be here much longer, but he will always remember how the evening light falls across this Cornish bay, in shades of sapphire, ivory and misty mauve. Amber, turquoise, ultramarine, vermilion and maroon lie hidden in the depths of those ever-moving waves, and are suddenly revealed as the rollers swirl below the little town that dreams in opalescent light above the dark-mouthed caves and alabaster sands.

The wonder and beauty of it bewilders him, touches a deep chord that is strange and sweet and sad. Half-remembered words vibrate across his heart. What was that chap singing in the canteen?—queer-looking fellow with red hair—played well——

" Does she love me . . . yes or no . . .?"

Puffs of smoke gather and fade across the far-off fields, lost in apricot light. There goes the little train. His letter will be in London with the new day.

Chapter VII

THE WEDDING

IT IS MISS JOLLY'S WEDDING-DAY. A BLUE AND GOLDEN SUMMER afternoon when Pollyon's whiteness gleams high above the sea like curving pearls on a green velvet gown.

Her fiancé, the Air Force Sergeant of the dictionary and poached eggs, has forty-eight hours' leave. Time is short; life is shorter still. The bride was born here. She has scarcely left her home and even now she will return there, after their honeymoon, alone.

All Pollyon, clad in their best, drift towards the tiny Cornish church on this stainless day. Not the big electrically lit building, close to the canteen, but a sort of baby church which must have been old when this little town was young. Squat-towered, thick-walled, it has, for all its smallness, an air of indestructible strength. The pews are short and few, solid oak faded to the mellowness of autumn leaves, silky with the smoothness of age, and the flagged floor between them gives off a delicious coolness. No ornament, no carvings sully the simplicity of the lovely roof and pillars, the plain pulpit and roughly hewn font. No flicker of brass disturbs the utter serenity of that opaline interior with its milky candles and altar vases of unpainted clay. The one stained window is, as yet, unwoken by the wheeling sun. Palm trees raise their spiky heads with a touch of savagery against sober English yews, and a tangle of bright flowers riot among the gravestones.

A scarlet bus, stridently new and hideous against such a setting, disgorges unnaturally clean men wearing restricting collars. They carry musical instruments, silvery bright in the afternoon light; they tune up cheerfully without preamble. Children perch on the overhanging wall, a good vantage-point from which to see the bride. The deserted churchyard, that has slept in empty sunlight for five hundred summers, suddenly becomes the scene of life and colour.

A cricket match is about to take place across the road. Soldiers are setting up the stumps, and as the XI musters, one by one, they stroll over to listen to the band, and exchange pleasantries with the local inhabitants. One portly player, to whom the trappings of matrimony are obviously but a side issue, is making imaginary cuts with his bat for the benefit of gaping youths who ogle the dressed-up girls. Sport and women. The beginning and end of male interest.

The band music dies away. Four middle-aged men in neat dark clothes are sitting on the churchyard wall joking with their friends.

" Give us a song now, 'tis little enough music we hear these days."

" No time, the bride's cummin'."

" Women is always late. Come on!"

They slither down, stand roughly grouped together, one hums a note, then their voices waken and swell together in a flood of harmony.

This is no casual sing-song, but a trained quartet, each man taking his part. The bass is a burly fellow and the depth of his voice seems fathomless. Down, down, he goes, without effort, then up and up to meet the flute-like tenor.

The chatter is hushed. No whisper of sound breaks the ripe silence. It is so still that even the tiny sigh of the singers drawing breath can be faintly heard. This is real music and how everyone responds to its exquisite simplicity. A soldier who is hammering the cricket stumps straightens his back, listening intently: gossiping women stand still as tombstones, even the tough young airmen, standing about the porch, who have come to see their comrade married, are enjoying it. The complete unexpectedness of hearing the well-known, well-loved phrases is both strange and disturbing.

> I did but see her passing by,
> And yet I love her till I die.

The quartet stand with hands thrust into their pockets, carelessly, without embarrassment, happily unaware that their voices are a gift from God. No touch of commercialism, the curse of art, casts its shadow upon them. The audience, to whom the proceedings are doubtlessly familiar, applaud loudly, but our enthusiasm is unbounded. A host of memories have stirred in their sleep. Memories of evenings round the piano and voices that now sing no more.

We approach, diffidently, as strangers, to express appreciation.

" Will you sing again? It's lovely, such a treat to hear it."

They look at each other, then at their watches. " We'll have another tune when they come out of church. Thank you; glad you liked it."

" Yes, I'm a miner. There's nothing else here, but farm-labouring. One of the tin mines is a mile and a quarter under the sea. The work is hard and dangerous, but it's in our blood. We can't get away from it."

Do they sing as they work? He laughs. " Yes, miners always sing. Don't know why. To pass away the time down there in the dark, maybe." His speaking voice has great depth, and there is light and shadow in it tinging the most commonplace utterances with charm. He pronounces his *s*'s as *z*'s with a pleasing softness.

Where do they learn their music? " Organist, he teaches us, but the practising is difficult, as the miners all work in different shifts." Some leave their homes, he says, for mining in Canada, and South Africa, but they always come back. " And travel don't change them."

These men who wrest a living from the bowels of the earth look tanned and healthy. Their eyes are clear. Yet half their working lives are spent in fetid darkness, groping blindly in enclosed spaces, unable even to stand at their full height. Disease ravages them; mutilation, entombment may come at any moment. In spite of this, or perhaps because of it, they sing.

More soldiers, shirt-sleeved ready for cricket, come upon the scene and add to the gaiety.

" Wot's on 'ere then?"

" Weddin'. Miss Jolly, pretty gal that helps in the canteen, and a flyin' fella."

No fuss whatever is made of bridegrooms. A friend gives him a drink before he starts for the ceremony. He fills his notecase with all available cash, slaps his trouser pocket to make sure of the ring. That's about all. The Royal West Hamptonshires amble towards the pitch, leisured, cheerful, without care. Girlish glances follow them, hopefully; to be in your best clothes among a lot of soldiers is too good a chance to waste, they feel.

But what man will look at a girl when there's a ball about?

Men are scarce now. Great chunks of the Army aren't much good. They come and go too quickly. Half of them are married already. The others only need a girl to have fun with; they march away next day and never come back.

And yet, and yet it's soldiers the women want. In peace or war it's always the same. All down the ages. A sort of magic hangs about them. They are rough and strong and clean and always laughing, everything a man should be, and so seldom is. Their maleness has not been watered down by poor living or indoors-y ways. And men soften quickly in little stuffy kitchens that are all kippers and curling-pins.

Country courtships are slow, utterly different from the whirl-wind tactics of the soldiery. It takes months to get even within range of the target. Then comes the opening move of walking out, long speechless Sunday afternoons, when understanding ripens, but no word comes. It may be months before the engagement is announced. Easter, Boxing Day or Whit-Monday, being favoured days, as public holidays suitable for merry-making and marrying. Then, at least a year, and often two, elapses, before the altar is reached. It is all very deliberate and suitable and hopelessly dull. Now with these soldiers there is no delay. They may be slow in some ways, but not in love. Women enjoy being swept off their

feet and treated crudely.   A C 3 wooing isn't worth having, and
it's all many women ever know.   But soldiers are A 1 men.
Different altogether.

The guests arrive slowly.   Mrs. Treloon, who aims, not quite
like Hitler, at world, but Pollyon domination, wears a creation of
pale green with coral make-up.   Everyone looks extremely smart
and quite unnatural, with the exception of the Royal Air Force,
the Girl Guides and the Boy Scouts, who are happily immune from
personal idiosyncrasies of apparel by reason of their uniforms.   Mr.
Blunt is hardly recognisable; his navy suit, immaculate collar and
rigid hat give him a fenced-in look that is wholly foreign.   He is
encompassed by squads of relations, all hampered by overtight
shoes and Sunday hats.   Farmer Jolly is leading in the winner.

Here comes the bride!   A white figure, gilded by the afternoon
light.   And as she enters the cool dimness of the church where she
was christened the organ greets her.

Who would true valour see, let him come hither.

The forceful words and robust tune fit the occasion exactly
since the Royal Air Force are here in strength.   The company of
heaven.   Women with their hearts in the past and girls with their
minds on the future sing with cheerful vigour.

Here's one will constant be, come wind, come weather.

A shaft of sunlight caresses the bridal pair, warming the walls
and pillars with creamy radiance.   The music dies away, and, in
the momentary silence that follows, the crack of a cricket bat and
soldiers' laughter drifts in through the open door.

"Till death us do part."

He slips the gold ring on her finger, symbol of eternity.   They
kneel before the simple altar with its wooden cross flanked by
country flowers.   The sun pours in through the stained glass
window like living blood casting scarlet splashes on the flagged
floor, over the bridal gown.   But there are other colours as well.
Madonna blue, pure and calm as a baby's eyes; green, bright as
May meadows; long shafts of topaz light that fall across the airman's
shoulders, burnishing his hair.   He has become almost an old
friend and it is strange to see him in this new setting without his

dictionary or paying-in book, cumbered with shopping commissions for his friends.

The Duchess looks at the kneeling uniformed figure remembering another man's shoulders, another man's arms, and sunlight, such as this, on the day he left her alone for ever. Mrs. Blunt wishes she had an airman son like that, one of her own, a very part of Mr. Blunt and herself, something that had grown of their welded life, as well as the little waifs that had been thrown into it. Mrs. Treloon stares at the flat blue back, and wide shoulders, thinking how nice they would look in her bedroom, while the linen draper notes Miss Jolly's fresh, unaided beauty and natural grace with admiring envy.

And I think of Nick, all across the years. Waving to him as his ship slipped out of Tilbury, not seeing the glorious May morning but the world merely as a dark place set with traps for his destruction. Meeting him, after six endless months, in Murree Hills, watching that first sunset turn the far-off Indus into golden fire. Watching him ride into Meanee Barracks at the head of his men, and then, at last, seeing Norney Rough and saying "We must have it."

It is all the small intimacies of shared life that give meaning and depth to it, not the early thunder of emotions that provide the writers and film actors with such solid incomes.

Women carry a thousand pictures of some man in their hearts, tiny pictures of the way in which he lights his pipe; turns his head; stretches out in his favourite chair; puts on an overcoat, tugging down the under one with his left hand, and pulling up the outer one with his right. Absurd things to remember, and yet they live always.

These two will come to know that, and the sight of them brings such thoughts vividly to mind.

Then they pass down the aisle into sea-scented air where the miners wait for them at the lych gate. Their blended voices swell to meet man and wife with the old madrigal:

> My true love hath my heart, and I have his,
> By just exchange one for another given;
> I hold his dear, and mine he cannot miss;
> There never was a better bargain driven;
> My true love hath my heart, and I have his.

His heart in me keeps him and me in one,
My heart in him his thoughts and senses guides;
He loves my heart, for once it was his own;
I cherish his because in me it bides;
My true love hath my heart, and I have his.

And then a brisk man marshals the wedding party to be immortalised upon pasteboard and in the Pollyon Press. They crowd together looking exactly as if all their teeth are to be extracted. But he is a sensible photographer and takes snapshots " unbeknownst" with, undoubtedly, happier effects.

A huge black car of ancient design, enlivened by white streamers and rosettes, bears the couple away and we all follow behind, with the miners' music echoing in our hearts.

Miss Jolly had said: " We're just having a few friends in afterwards, do come." But this is no cup-of-tea-and-bun affair.

Long trestle tables are set out in the two living-rooms, and in the great stone-floored kitchen behind. There a Union Jack has been hung across the one end to hide the sinews of the house, gas-cooker and sink. Gleaming copper pans cluster above the wide hospitable hearth where the logs of five hundred winters have given warmth. The dresser is hung with blue china, the wide window-sills are rimmed with flowers. A great oak chest glows like copper beech leaves against the whitewashed walls.

What a spread! How can Mrs. Jolly have made such food in war-time? Curry puffs, light as air; lobster patties; dozens of individual jellies, pink, yellow, red, fruit-filled. The very thing for little hot Girl Guides. Sandwiches of many kinds. Sardine; tomato; cheese, all beautifully ticketed. And a large plum cake, innocent of sugar, but dark with richness and a small British flag flying proudly from it. Something that is in the British people will keep that flag flying, tattered and torn maybe, paid for by agony and tears, but flying still. The day will come when the beasts have been beaten, bludgeoned, blockaded into defeat and disaster.

There are bowls of fruit salad and cream.

" Not real cream but the best we can do in war-time," she smiles.

Yet it is Cornish cream. The best in the world. The quality of Cornish food is so high. Even in war-time it seems better than what we had in Surrey. Why is this? Can it be that the glorious air affects such things as eggs, peas, tomatoes, lettuce, and even poultry? The chicken patties (not chicken at all, but dowagers of several springs, so Mrs. Jolly whispers confidentially to us) have a rich sweet flavour of their own. Is the sea air responsible? Do fowls respond favourably to Atlantic breezes?

It must be the air. No living thing could sicken in this Cornish corner. Even cabbages and carrots become handsomer, more tasty by reason of its caress. It may be that with our island folk some subtle change is wrought so that the pleasures of the palate are quickened. The extreme simplicity of war-time food doubles the importance of its excellence.

Farm hands, sheepish in their finery, drink cider and beer in a corner with intense enjoyment. Holidays seldom come their way and this is a great occasion. It's wonderful to eat lobster patties and plum cake on a weekday instead of cleaning out the cowsheds; pleasant to sit at ease watching all the bustle inside the cool, friendly house, to see the airmen, face to face on their feet, instead of swooping over the fields, high against the sky, like dragon-flies at play.

" They looks like we did, when we were buoys, doan 'em?" whispers one to another.

" Ah! but they ain't. There's never bin any like 'em before."

Yes there has. The ancestors of these British men who fought at Minden, Trafalgar, Waterloo, all had the same flame burning in their hearts, the unquenchable beacon that shines brightest in the darkest hours. What is it? Perhaps it is tradition—that strange thing that we cannot live without. Such men never have been beaten. They never will be. All the world knows that. None better than the Germans. They know to their cost that Britishers are stubborn, resilient, strong, unafraid: in a word, unbeatable.

These Cornish fields will be ours, always, though battles may be fought above and upon them. Brutal hands are outstretched to pierce the bright sapphire and silver armour that belts our shores, the smiling summer sea that is our sure shield.

The bride moves among the guests with charming naturalness. The bridegroom is a foreigner, unknown to any of them and in peace-time they would be slow to welcome him. But this is war and he is one of heaven's company. They hold out their hands and shake his warmly.

What a perfect wife she will make. She has everything, seemingly. Good looks, physical charm and ability, being a perfect cook, clever housekeeper, capable dressmaker. She can milk a cow, ride, and play bridge. Perhaps the war will teach us the value of domesticity, the vital importance, to the nation and the individual, of well-run homes. When war's machinery is stilled girls may be trained as domestic workers; given a uniform and salary according to skill and experience. Let's hope we never go back to paying some stupid unwilling girl £52 a year for breaking all the china, and failing to clean the saucepans. Far better give a 30s. weekly wage to a trained worker, who can make delicious soup out of next to nothing and understands the importance of a balanced diet.

They want their evenings! That is the cry. Their evenings! Their evenings! Take them! Take them! Who wants what is grudged? We don't want your evenings. Give us willing, efficient service. We'll pay you well; feed you well; house you well. What's wrong with that? Nothing.

But the lazy breakfast-in-bed mistress who does nothing and keeps a parlourmaid out of idleness or snobbery deserves no domestic help at all. Because she is not pulling even her own weight. Women are only entitled to servants when they are doing worthwhile work themselves. She who makes all the family clothes and teaches her children, cannot, obviously, cook and clean for the family unaided. Any assistance she has is fully earned.

But the read-the-newspaper-in-the-morning—play-bridge-in-the-afternoon wife is just a contemptible social parasite.

Let her get up at 6.30 a.m. when the mercury measures fifteen degrees of frost, and stand in snow to shovel the coke to fill her kitchen boiler, clean two rooms, cook breakfast for the family by 8 a.m. Then she'd see life through energy's eyes. A revelation indeed.

Women of every class will always want a husband, children, a home. That is just as certain as the sun is in the sky. It is the old, old law. Unalterable. Does shop and factory life of peace-time provide a good training for that? What sort of wives do such tea-and-bun girls make? They can't even fry bacon and no man will put up with badly fried bacon for long. Too many other women know how to do it. Not to mention his mother.

If anything makes a bride see red it is to be told that she cannot fry bacon as well as her mother-in-law. A situation which could never, never happen to Miss Jolly.

At last it is all over. The bride has changed into her travelling frock, and together they face the barrage of thrown rose leaves. "Good luck to you!" All gather at the gate to wave farewell. The car rolls down the rough white road towards a new world. What did the bridegroom give the bride? Wishes come true.

A feeling of flatness follows any wedding, except one's own. Guests walk home in their best shoes, which are probably none too comfortable, vaguely dissatisfied. Women who haven't got husbands wish they had; and those who are blessed with mates wish he or she were a little different. Not quite so homely; not quite so worldly; rather warmer, or rather colder. Impossible to get it all right. Ridiculous to try. And yet nothing in the world matters half so much. The pace and demands of life have increased so that efficiency matters now as never before. Food, clothes, money need clever management if Romance is to be kept alive. The 1918 war wife lay in bed watching her 'on leave' husband pack and dress while someone else cooked their breakfast. But Mrs. Civil Defence 194– is up long before he wakes, brushing his uniform, cleaning his boots, brewing the coffee, frying the bacon ration for him as a matter of course. She is a calmer, steadier, saner person than her 1918 counterpart; restrained, disciplined.

And will she go mad when the killing is over, as girls and women did in the last war? No. Her relief and rejoicing will not be tainted with hysteria, drugs, drink or sordid love-affairs. She will go on working, with, or without, the man who sleeps now deeply, thankfully, in her room.

In a few hours he will be gone.

The Crescent Hotel vestibule, never beautiful, looks hideous now after the warmth and colour and youth just left behind in the farmhouse. The children are bathing with small new-found friends, so an additional dreariness infects the atmosphere.

"Letters!" The friendly postman holds out a pile. Balm in Gilead. Letters assume a new importance when half of life is left behind. Here is the Cleaner's bill. All wrong as usual—"To cleaning 3 pillows." That was paid three months ago. But no receipt is at hand to verify this. They are all lying neatly docketed in my desk two hundred miles away and Norney Rough is shut this week because Nick is in Suffolk. So I must communicate with Kum Kleen Company. A waste of valuable paper.

Alice writes:

" The carratts are up have you got a receipe for bottling carratts because carratts will be scarce this winter. The laundry as lost two of my best aprons will you get them back for me please afternoon ones. We want some more coke and what shall I do about the carratts.

Yours truely,
ALICE WILLING."

" What shall I do about the Colonel the doctor says I shall be fit for the factory in about a fortnight and I don't know what to do about him as I know it would worry you if he only had Mrs. Cod to do for him so what shall I do?"

Nothing, Alice. I shall be back to see to the carratts and the Colonel.

It is not easy to run a house in Surrey from Cornwall, even for a very short time, especially if you have a Martha-ish mind, that keeps wondering if Alice is putting disinfectant down the kitchen sink daily? Is she mending properly for Nick or has he lost the waist-cord of all his pyjamas and is he too shy to ask her to replace them? Does the fishmonger send fair weight? Do spiders make merry in the silence of empty nurseries? Has any rapacious tradesman discovered our absence and, dismayed by the halving of our account, is he busily adding halfpence to every penny? Do stale ends clutter the breadpan, and does rain beat in through forgotten open windows on to the old table that was in Grandmother's nursery? Has the garage tap been repaired? Will Grind, now undisputed Minister of Agriculture, remember to sow turnips directly the potatoes are lifted? Has Nick paid the coke merchant twice or not at all?

What a blessing that the bathrooms were not repainted just before the war. Now even their ventilators must be kept shut: steam is ruining the walls and Alice is so bomb conscious that she opens no crack of window from moonup till dawn. Does the blackbird still perch on the larch's topmost branch singing to the fading yellow sky and deepening stars?

Absurd to worry an overworked man with such questions. But he answers them all without being asked. All this and more. His letters are wonderful. They tell me exactly what I want to know. What he had for breakfast; which flowers are out in the wood and if the sun is shining.

The children burst in: "Letter from Dad? Read it! Read it!"

" Well, young people, I've got on one sock with a red pattern and the other with a blue. Oh dear! Oh dear! don't tell Mummy.

" There are hardly any flowers in the garden now and when I walked round this evening the honeysuckle said, ' What's the use of blooming when there isn't anyone to bloom for?' So I said, ' What about me?' and it answered: ' Well, there are the roses, and the carrots, and peas and lettuces, aren't they good enough for you?'

" I went for a walk through the wood with an envelope for Mummy and Black Sambo came out of his farm kennel and said: ' Where are Sally and Sue?'

" ' At the seaside, nice and cool in the sea,' and he barked:

" ' Well, it's too hot to walk with you, you must go alone.' Then a little rabbit scuttled up, quite slowly and whispered: ' I'll come with you. Where are Sally and Sue?'

" ' They are paddling in the sea.'

" ' What! can't they swim?'

" ' Sally can, and Sue says she can, but she can't.'

" ' I don't believe a word of it,' said the little rabbit.

" ' Are they as tall as me?' asked the big bracken, ' or as me?' echoed the little bracken.

" ' They are both just exactly the right size.'

" Then the trees nodded their heads and said, ' Come again and bring them with you.' As I walked slowly back a little bird sang— ' Shall I fly down and give them your love?'

" ' Do. Come back to a bird-crumb breakfast outside my door and I'll butter the bread for you as a treat.' And he flew away to the larch top calling: ' Come back! Come back!'

" ' Well,' yawned Sambo, as he lay stretched on the lawn, ' did you see anything?'

" ' Yes. I saw their footprints.'

" ' And what did they smell of?'

" ' Honeysuckle and pine needles and dew.'

" ' Ugh!' grunted Sambo."

What curious thoughts absent husbands provoke. The sight of a perfectly packed car, the luggage lashed on with firmness and exact balance; an opened book of detective stories; the smell of a cigar; apple tart (and, once, cream), sunshine after rain, instantly bring Nick to my mind, no matter if ten thousand miles or the length of the garden lie between us. And can he look any teddy bear in the face without a stab of loneliness?

Complaints of every kind are brought to him. "Just you look at my stockings," demands one of the typists, lifting high her skirts before the unwilling gaze of Surrey's A.R.P. officials. "It's the chairs, awful scratchy things, and Miss Whig's are just as bad, aren't they, dear?"

Miss Whig, whose best part is above the table, keeps her calves well hidden, but nods assent. Well, what to do? Scrap the chairs. Give them away, burn them! Anything for peace and ladderless legs. Now then, back to business. Where did those incendiaries fall last night?

"There are more bombs in Surrey offices than . . ."

But there is one bad bit of news. We are to keep hens. It is almost the first direct domestic order that Nick has ever given. There is no question of "What do you think?" "Shall we . . . etc.?" The hens are ordered. Their hideous little house erected "in the *far* corner of the wood".

Shop eggs may become as rare as the Koh-i-noor, therefore these silly clucking birds, whose sexual life is absurdly complicated and obscure, must defile every garden and backyard. Feeding hens in a cool summer frock, when somebody else has cooked their food and somebody else has cleaned their quarters, is a picturesque occupation. But England's summer is short and winter goes on and on and on. However, a ray of hope cheers the prospect of carrying food and water to our feathered friends on ice-bound winter mornings, fumbling with frozen fingers among potato peelings which must be cooked—as well as the family lunch. Hens need husbands. Then we can have a rooster, a bold gorgeous fellow with slim, high-stepping legs and a floppety knife-edged comb, scarlet as the rising sun to which he crows his greeting.

He swaggers about, treating his harem with supreme contempt, his mind far, far above such things as scrambled eggs.

Chanticleer, herald of each coming day. Who has not watched through an unending night of pain and heartbreaking suspense, waiting for the hope that comes as cock-crow ushers in the morning and the powers of darkness are defeated and overthrown? His shrill clarion call is the loveliest of all country sounds.

Friday—Alice's day out. She will soon be coming in, trotting up the lane on monstrous heels. Nick's supper will be laid on the sideboard. I can see the green mats, the white-walled room dappled with evening light. Cold beef; salad in a green bowl; apple tart; cut bread by the electric toaster, laid ready to his hand, and at 8.30 Alice will tittup home, in her plain smart clothes, with matching accessories that all miraculously cost but a few shillings the lot. She will snap on the kitchen wireless and the smell of coffee will perfume the house. Then she brings in the little Chinese cups, no, one cup, that fat green pot of milk; while all the evening sounds drift across the garden—rooks, going home. Soldiers walking in twos and threes, the night wind murmuring in the pines.

Alice watches the soldiers with mingled contempt and regret. Every girl in the village has a boy now. Why did she say No to the gardener seven years ago in her last place? True, he had adenoids and flat feet. But now she has no one. A bedroom in someone else's house is her only home. But she doesn't have a baby every year and everlasting backache like her sister. And her savings account is mounting, mounting. Old age is hell anyway, married or single. She kicks off her shoes, philosophically, and puts her feet up, listening to the nine o'clock news, while Nick writes very small cheques to the butcher, the milkman, some letters to the War Office. Then Alice pads up to bed in stockinged feet and Nick writes on, in the room that grows steadily shabbier. This year it was to have been distempered, the ceiling painted, but the months drag by, the war goes on, and interior decoration is a needless luxury.

Lavinia writes: "Mere has gone. Bashed to bits by bombs. Now we'll never know the sorrow of parting with it. Better this than that."

Her family have lived at Mere for three hundred years.

" Great-grandfather's portrait was left on the wall untouched."
He was one of Wellington's Generals. . . . A good omen.
" The house was empty. A week later it would have been a
maternity home. We were always lucky, except over money
and now that doesn't matter any more.

" The grey stone all tumbled about the garden is still lovely.
German bombs could not destroy it. So we shall build a new
house out of the old one. Another, better Mere for our children
and theirs. Not a place of pillars and balustrades with a great
stone staircase, and cold corridors, but a living monument to the
dead days. And we've still got the land, the river, the trees."
Her old spirit flames up. " Now, at last, we can have new dining-
room curtains!"

Lavinia, years ago, riding up the drive with wind-tossed golden
curls, on a blue and yellow October day. The Mere terrace
spattered with scarlet coats, white breeches. Bowler-hatted girls
with glossy boots drive up, eager, careless, happy. Grooms walk
their horses up and down, up and down under the thinning elms,
and then horses, hounds drift away across the park a great living
wave of white, black, grey-brown and scarlet, moving over the
wind-dried grass.

Then Lavinia as a bride and all London craning to glimpse her
golden beauty. Lavinia, now, amid the ruins of her home,
planning a new way of life. Triumphant. Unafraid.

Chapter VIII

THE CANTEEN

SUNDAY EVENING. A GALE SWEEPS THE STREET. RAIN LASHES THE
canteen windows, blotting out sky and cliffs. The house, shabby
enough when the sun shines, is darkly sinister in such a storm;
doors rattle, draughts eddy underneath, stone floors are clammy
with reeking damp and the rooms are so dark that a light is needed.
There is an underground feeling about the kitchen as if water
were rising in the cellars below, the sad smell of mildew that
breathes of neglect—decay. The sound of a dripping tap heightens
the dreariness—and emphasises the stillness of the dank scullery.

Our mackintoshes stream into the sink, no umbrella can be
hoisted to-day, squelching shoes are turned up to drain, and sodden
stockings peeled off. Dry ones donned.

The wind moans, screams, wails about the little town with
furious malevolent intensity, making sport of the few pedestrians
who are about, ballooning out their clothes, buffeting them hither
and thither like giant leaves, purposeless, unresisting.

Great grey rollers gather with terrible strength and hurl themselves, with thunderous magnificence, against solid rocks that
splinter them into a million jets which fly up, up, then fall, are
sucked back only to gather fresh force and rise again, undaunted
by any barrier.

Mrs. Blunt buttons on a useful overall which is a clumsy garment
all out of spirit with the times—long, dark grey, needlessly full,
like the overcoats that German Generals wear on manœuvres when
it rains.   Quite different from Mrs. Treloon who is always dressed
in review order.   She dries her legs on the small towel that she
sensibly brought with her.

" No men will come in to-night; they couldn't stand on the
cliff path in such weather.   Good chance for stocktaking.   There's
never time to do it in the week."

So we begin to check and sort the stores, making lists of needful
purchases, brushing out the cake tins, doing all the small jobs
that can't be tackled on busy days.   Bars of yellow soap are cut
up into usable sizes, and stacked separately to harden.   Empty
soft-drink bottles are sorted and put out for collection; new ones
unpacked.   Tea and sugar canisters, lowered after the heavy
demands of Saturday night, are replenished.   All the tables need
washing with soap and hot water, their shiny oilcloth surfaces
being dulled by hard usage.   And there is time to scrub the ashtrays.   Nothing but total immersion can kill the staleness that
hangs about them.

Then some extra sweeping and dusting is done, but on this
particular afternoon nothing can be thrown out into the garden
for purification.   Turnouts can only be successfully done when
the ground is dry.   Soldier folk never spring-clean.   They move
so often that cobwebs cannot thicken.   But the result is the same.
Everything is taken up from one place and put down in another
and a sort of healthy air of change pervades houses and rooms
and minds when all this has been achieved.   Mrs. Treloon's
excellent legs protrude from the cupboard before which she kneels,
busily sorting tins.   Her slightly muffled voice runs on—

" They hadn't any swim suits, but I think they were officers;
six tins sardines, eight matches, two pounds sugar, that right?"

" Yes."   Mrs. Blunt, to whom clothed and unclothed men
fall into much the same category, replies benignly, " It isn't

easy to get bathing trunks now, and they must be cooler without."

" Oh yes, but it may put ideas into their heads."

Surely that is where all ideas should be. Ask the colonel, ask the sergeant, tell the marines.

Mrs. Blunt cares for none of these things. She brushes the hair off her sticky forehead, licks the stub of her pencil and writes " Six sardines, eight matches . . . two sugar . . . three tea. . . ."

" Pity she's let herself go," remarks Mrs. Treloon to her husband one night, satin nightwear rippling from her shoulders. " Can't think why women let themselves go."

Mr. Treloon sinks upon his pillow wondering why he hasn't. She comes out of the cupboard, chatting still.

" . . . and I told her it wasn't ladylike to tweak a boy's ears, but she never took a bit of notice. . . .

" . . . Yes, his underclothes were sewn on . . . just rags, and his head was alive. He's a different creature now, five pounds fatter, you'd never know him. . . ."

Chairs and tables are pulled out, every corner dusted with extra thoroughness. But we don't move the wireless, it's far too delicate an affair to tamper with. Leave that to Sergeant Sly's skilful hands. He's the sort of man who must have something to care for. The cure for bitterness lies that way. His twisted nature has no chance to straighten because of the enforced idleness that has been thrust upon him. That's why he hates the parrot. Even to have conquered Daisy would have been something, but Spike forestalled him. And Sergeant Sly will be second to no man.

The wireless is an antique affair of maddening moods—rather like the hospital cook, who has attracted Sly, not by beauty or charm, but by sheer contrariness. He will, in time, master her, as he has mastered this absurd contraption of wood and wire which was presented with much ceremony and accepted with profuse thanks. Nobody else could get a word out of it. Daisy's few phrases, at unexpected intervals, have caused far more interest and amusement than this belching box.

Half of the R.A.F. have dismantled and reassembled it; the Ploughshire Regiment have done the same. Many of the West Hamptonshires have poked and probed. No use. But Sergeant

Sly instantly learnt all its secrets. Even machinery responds to his fatal charm.

"This is a record of Mr. Wendell Wilkie's speech." But the well-modulated voice dies away, to be followed by awful screeches, groans, hiccups. Is Mr. Wendell Wilkie unwell? Perhaps that is the roar of the populace welcoming him? Maybe it is his plane arriving? But it is encouraging that the thing has come to life. And to have made contact with America has added a cubit to our stature.

How soon, how soon, shall we hear "This is London calling the British Empire," and we shall know, wherever we may be, that the lights are streaming out from Buckingham Palace and cottage homes. Then Europe's enslaved millions will lift up their heads and behold the miracle of dawn.

Shall we ever listen to the news when the war is over? What could be worth hearing once all our men are safe?

Will it ever matter again if a deep depression is approaching over Iceland, thereby threatening to ruin tennis finals? There was a time when such trivialities seemed disastrous. Will feeling run high about the weather for Ascot or Lord's? Shall we care if the blue and white outfit will pass muster for another summer, having shared stocking coupons with schoolgirl daughters as a matter of course? The world will be so full of newness that anything old will have an almost prehistoric value. New ways, new days, will be dished out like hot, indigestible buns.

Meanwhile small tasks must still be done. The linoleum-covered floor looks bare and cold in the chilly twilight, as do the long rows of clean cups arrayed on the shiny blue-and-white table cover. How welcoming Norney Rough would be on such a night; a log fire leaping on the brick hearth; Sally playing the piano with increasing tunefulness and confidence in the flame-lit room with flowers everywhere. Nick in his grandfather's old chair with Sue on his lap, a book in her hands. "Now tell me everyfing about God, there's a picture of Him here, in this little cwadle all among the wushes. Look! Isn't He sweet!" and Moses would be held out for inspection.

Can't we all remember looking at Moses in his basket on Sunday evenings, long, long ago? It is one of childhood's pictures that is the last to fade.

There. And now it is all finished. Shelves dusted and straightened. Sardine tins turned carefully over, so that the top layer of fish shall not be left high and dry above the oil, cleaning materials grouped tidily together, beside the dustpan. The kitchen has been well cleaned, but nothing short of entire repainting could make it smart. However, it is neat and orderly for our backdoor callers. A policeman came to tea yesterday. The Queen's Black Lancers, no longer embellished with manes and tails and spurs, but enclosed by fast and formidable vehicles, wanted to get from one end of Cornwall to another, quickly, and a car was in their way outside the canteen.

Thump, thump in the passage. Quite a different tread from Army boots, slower, heavier. And then, " This your car, Madam?" " No, haven't got one."—" No."—" No." Not Guilty. So he pokes his head into the men's room. The owner is obviously not there. We look outside to see the burly Lancers trundling the little car about as if it were a child's toy barrow. They lift it bodily on to the pavement, right against the window. There! Now the road's clear. Off they go upon the King's business, grinning, waving to the policeman who stumps into the kitchen, where he has left his notebook in truly rustic fashion.

" Like a cup of tea?"

" Thanks, I would that." His height and dignity and general largeness adds great distinction to the poor surroundings. Small wonder that cooks like to entertain policemen; a kitchen seems to be their natural setting.

Sometimes the children bring in the daily paper, or bunches of flowers for the tables. Once they are allowed in for tea, a rare treat. They squat on turned-up boxes, munching buns, peering through the hatch to catch a glimpse of the men. As they buy their lemonade at the counter, Alf, who doubtless thinks Sue is an evacuated Londoner, asks her, as one outcast to another,

" Well, 'ow are you keepin'?"

" All wight, fanks."

" Good lemonade, ain't it?"

" Um . . . m . . . m . . . m. Lovely. I don't like the sort what pricks."

" Ginger beer?"

" Yes. I hate that."

Bar loungers not being permissible she scuttles away.

"This is a dirty kitchen. Howwible. All dark. Not a bit like Norney Wuff, is it, Sally?"

"No. But they've got a parrot." The logic of women. Tea over, they inspect Daisy who is roused to rage at the sight of two little girls. She evidently hates children with all the strength of her small contrary brain.

"I don't like it; I had warver a cat." Sue backs away from the lowered, threatening head.

We bring chairs to the kitchen table and drink our tea, eat a slice of yesterday's left-over cake, and very good too, made out of dates and dripping by Mrs. Blunt. There isn't much to talk about as we knit, wash up our crockery, listen to the relentless rain. Then the paralysing effect of inaction sets in. The chilly, darkening kitchen, hideous for all our efforts to improve it, and the rare silence of the rooms, empty now for more than four hours, is deeply depressing. All man-made sounds are obliterated by the fury of the storm. No footfalls in the passage; no voices in the street; no planes droning over the harbour. Not even the murmur of the bus grinding up the long hill. Only the click of knitting needles, and then Mrs. Treloon's voice, suddenly loud in the long-stretched stillness.

"Seems waste of time sitting here. There's nothing more to do, but we can't leave the place. Some man might drop in. We needn't all three stay. There's a good preacher to-night, worth hearing."

They have both already attended divine service; so it is suggested that I might like to go. The granite church almost joins the canteen. A blessing on such a night.

There are many unfortunate and neglected parishes in England. I found myself in such a one that never-to-be-forgotten summer Sunday when it seemed that nothing but a miracle could save our hemmed-in Army. A miracle did save them.

It was in the West Country. But not here, nor in a Methodist church. A few perfunctory prayers were gabbled by a clergyman who seemed drugged by their familiarity. A sermon of twenty minutes was delivered about St. Paul. Never once did the preacher mention the peril of our Army and our Empire. No word of hope or comfort was offered. The National Anthem was not sung.

Happily our tongues and hearts and souls can speak for themselves. So turning elsewhere for light I found it instantly in the Methodist church. This particular one is new to me, a lofty building reached by many stone steps which are now thronged with people. It is difficult to get inside, though the wild weather might well have kept people at home. Seats are filled fifteen minutes before the service begins. Chairs for latecomers fringes the aisles. Many soldiers are in the congregation, and there is a large mixed choir.

A small man in plain black, with no incense, no theatrical trimmings to play upon his listeners' emotions, conducts the service. His extempore prayers are brief, comprehensive, absolutely to the point. It is plain to see that the fighting men, and British traditions, come first with him.

And then he enters the pulpit. He stands very still, his hands upon the ledge in front of him—and begins to speak. What is the secret of the extraordinary strength that comes from his voice and personality? He is inspired. He sees something above and beyond his listeners, the plain building with its pale walls. What is it? His unshakable belief infects and spreads through the congregation like a fire.

" . . . he that hath no sword let him sell his garment and buy one." The words ring out resolute, clear. The flame that burns in him sets smaller hearts than his ablaze with courage and determination. He is a true patriot, intoxicated with a passionate love for Britain—" the last bastion of freedom in a tottering world." Here is a man who can give and give from the inexhaustible wells of his own spirit. No " love-and-forgive-your-enemy" preacher this, but a hater of the " foul pagan beast that we unite to destroy." He tells us that we must learn to hate—learn to loathe the lust and greed and brutality that we are fighting to stamp out and that no taint of easy tolerance must weaken the will to win.

Encouraging words to hear from a pulpit.

The Methodist Church has its finger on the pulse of the moment. It produces men of fire, faith and independence, who have not become bogged in the dullness of repetition. It's not enough to read the same prayers again and again. We know them all. We want something now to catch hold of, to be shown bigger, better things.

What a pity it is such preachers as these Methodists are so rare. Men who understand the dangers, delights and difficulties of everyday existence and do not withdraw themselves into a sort of holy harbour, mere onlookers of the battle and shipwreck strewn all about them.   They are stout-hearted, understanding men, sympathetic with those who are groping for guidance.   Their personalities and character command interest, respect, for they are true examples of all that is best and highest in human nature.   Models of behaviour and belief.

The very presence of this Pollyon minister is an inspiration and gives us something of his serenity and strength.   We have never needed it more than now, when life is a sort of all-in wrestling match.   I have never seen " all-in" wrestling and do not quite know what it means, but the phrase seems to fit the adventure of living exactly.   An immense fight against everything, especially oneself.   Not a disagreeable, bitter battle, but a never-ending struggle for understanding, facing the darkness squarely, searching for the light beyond, and it's hard to find.   We feel that we have " no sword."

There is painfully little that many of us can do, only the same small tasks, again and again, but nothing that is big enough to be really satisfying.   Knitting for the Forces and prisoners, sewing for half-naked evacuees, scrubbing the canteen sink.   Useful, but not nearly enough.   It must be wonderful to see the bombs and planes leave the factories, to be able to say " my work is in them," to know that each one means death to Germany.

Yet young children can't be left.   So many women are trying to be fathers, as well as mothers now, since father, and all he stands for, has been swept away.   Canteen work can be a pleasant form of suffocation.   Handing tea to soldiers is better than doing nothing, but it is only a small job.   It seems large enough when you are on your legs from six till ten o'clock without a break, washing up, taking orders, checking accounts, wiping up the coffee that someone spills over the floor.

But all this effort does not fall into the category of what really matters.   It in no way helps to defeat Germany.   To be perfectly honest it is an outlet which hundreds of women welcome.   The men benefit, which is important.   Perhaps the warmth, friendliness and little touch of comfort is a source of added strength to them. That's worth a lot. And a great many women can't do more. They can only give a few hours daily or weekly to some good cause, and for them canteen work is fitting and useful. Clubs for Dominion men, canteens at ports and London stations fall under a different heading. They are really needed. But buttering buns in this little town is not "war work." Only a tiny job which may help to keep Pollyon's memory green in the hearts of a few soldiers.

And it's easy to work in a crowd. The general stir and bustle and being one of many lessens monotony and increases the power of output. There's no temptation to slack off when the pace is hot and a sort of personal pride stiffens resistance to fatigue.

Could one soldier march for many, many hours all by himself? Yes, but his effort would be nearly doubled. What keeps him going when his lungs are bursting and his throat is a cindery hell? The men in front, behind, all about him. They sweep him on, inexorably.

It's difficult to stand, and work, and fight alone. Difficult to lash an exhausted mind and body on and on and on when there is nobody at all to encourage, inspire and cheer. Thousands of women are doing that now. Their husbands are killed, still fighting, or prisoners—and that means the grimmest fight of all. They are left to fend for their family on fast-dwindling incomes which may entirely vanish at any moment. The Empire's future lies in their children's dimpled hands. The upbringing of a child matters so much more than the mere producing of it. But with father gone the future is dark indeed. It is on these mothers that the cruellest burden falls. Their work is not for two, three, four years; they can't say "When this is all over we can have a good rest—a complete holiday." They are struggling to fight without weapons, as their men did before Dunkirk.

No one knows anything about these women whose day is not a matter of working hours but of all time. They wear no badge; no uniform. They can't ring up a friend and say "Do take my five o'clock shift to-day because we are all ill." There is no one who will look after three children with whooping cough and a mother with influenza. Volunteers are not forthcoming for a job like that, even in war. It's not exciting or well paid; just dull and very hard. Kind? Oh, well, it's just as kind to hand tea to soldiers.

No, it's not!

What a difficult time most women are having when there isn't much of anything, working, waiting in cities, villages and little towns, eking out the milk, the coal, the marge, wondering why baby's cough doesn't get better and if Willy's shoes will last another month. They walk from shop to shop collecting the rations and one onion, wondering if there'll be a couple of tomatoes or a pound of apples for the children. It's a long time since they tasted fruit. They peer into their shabby purses to see just how much is left. Yes, sixpence for the War Savings this week. That's good.

There is one thing that no woman ever wants to see again when the war is over and that's a shopping basket.

Wives turn on the wireless as they bend over the weekly wash-tub waiting for the postman. There he is! Just coming!

" One for me?"

" Not to-day."

How slowly the week passes in little rooms where no man comes.

The Canteen, on my return from church, or rather, chapel, is, surprisingly, full of movement. Some dozen men are going on leave by the midnight train and got a lift in from a lorry.

" How long can we stay here? It's cold and wet on the station."

" We'll keep open for you until eleven-thirty." Mrs. Blunt is about to make tea. Raindrops glisten on their rough uniform. Their faces and knuckles are red and chilled. The black empty grate is a reproach. Coal. Is there any? Yes, an old bucket full in the scullery—thick with dust. There's no wood, only a smart grocer's box of much value containing salvage paper.

But the men are wet and we must dry them. What will happen to that box when it leaves here? It could have no more fitting end than to warm the troops. So the elderly coal, the precious box and the old sugar cartons are quickly assembled, ignited. They blaze up with unexpected success.

The men are obviously grateful, they settle down happily to food and newspapers for a couple of hours.

Eight forty-five. " This is the National Anthem of France." Strange how National Anthems spring from the soul of the country they represent. Isn't the Marseillaise, with its light and shade, exactly typical of the French people? Haven't the slow sombre chords of God Save the King caught the characteristics of our country, deliberate, solid, unfailing? What do we feel when we hear that brave tune? Everything that makes our life worth while. All the things that last for ever.

The rain has stopped now, they'll have a dry walk to the station, that's good, and the wind that screamed about the walls is lessening. The soldiers collect their possessions, pay their bills, make ready to go.

"Good night, thank you very much for the fire."

"The fire, yes, that was grand, we're dry now." So the burning of the box was justified.

Lock-up time is a dreary business. I have never done it alone before. The sudden stillness that comes as the men's voices and footsteps die away is disconcerting. All the warmth and colour and meaning of this creaky old house goes out with them. Nothing is left but an empty shadowed shell in which the drip of the scullery tap sounds hammer loud. The fire has burnt out with satisfactory completeness.

Flick. Flick. Flick. The last light dies. A discreet torch reveals the door-lock. The key grates, harshly. Another day done.

The street is inky dark. Only the whitened kerb and faint flashlight act as guides. I battle along against the wind with ducked-down head, close to the houses, avoiding the " promenade" so lightly railed off from the sheer drop of cliffs. At the cross-roads it is difficult to find the way. The sea murmurs angrily like a hungry beast.

The echoing, deserted canteen, filmed with shadows, is not so grim as the Crescent lounge at midnight. Here, the lights burn on and on, and poor Miss Blossom cannot get her well-earned rest until the last chattering guest has climbed the stairs. There sits poor little Mr. Friske, chained to the bridge table with three flinty-faced females adding up scores and pushing shillings backwards and forwards with shrill persistence.

Madam, in untidy finery, is scolding poor Miss Blossom under her breath, not because fault-finding is needful. But the porter has given notice, and porters are as hard to come by in war as twelve pounds of butter. Miss Blossom doesn't mind. She only wants to go to bed. As soon as Madam is suited, she is leaving to look after two London boys, and help her mother on the farm. Her cushiony figure, shinily covered with stretched navy-blue silk, looks hardly suitable for the rigours of agricultural pursuits, but the land is in her blood and the " sure magic" of it is luring her from the Crescent Hotel ledger. Madam never will be suited and the hotel will not lie still beneath her thorny touch.

But the Crescent is shortly to change hands. Madam's brother, invalided out of the Army, needs a home and a job. Both are here waiting for him.

The siren disperses the bridge players and we stumble up the stairs. Sally and Sue lie with their " sons" in their arms. Sally's has lost all his chubbiness, his blond fur face is getting bald, his feet and " hands" have been renewed again and again with cut-up socks to match his torso. Sue's, younger and less loved, retains all the woolliness of his first youth.

" I don't love him quite so much now I can wead," his mother explains. She gladly tips her child out of bed in the mornings to pore over a picture book.

I turn out their light, go into the adjoining room, listening. Planes are overhead.

Their " lessons" are put out on the dressing-table. Sally's sums.

$$
\begin{array}{ll}
\text{\pounds}18 \quad 2 \quad 6 & \text{\pounds}2089 \ 16 \quad 9 \\
16 \ 19 \ 10 & \ 1897 \ 13 \ 10 \\
\hline
\text{\pounds}1 \quad 3 \quad 8 & \text{\pounds}292 \quad 3 \ 10 \qquad \text{Ah!}
\end{array}
$$

Paying back is a mystery that she cannot altogether master. This is better.

$$
\begin{array}{l}
\text{\pounds}1692 \ 19 \quad 9 \\
\ 889 \ 15 \ 10 \\
\hline
\text{\pounds}803 \quad 3 \ 11 \qquad \text{Right!}
\end{array}
$$

And the knitting is excellent. Wristlet ribbing for prisoners' gloves. The palm part is done by more experienced fingers. Sue is not yet bothered with the intricacies of correctness. She writes with enviable ease and freedom, unhampered by the toil of accuracy.

Do yOu LOve MEY es I DO I LOVEdad ThE CAT IS ON THE MAT LoVE FRoM SuE

Chapter IX

THE HOSPITAL

IT IS THE DUCHESS'S BIRTHDAY THIS WEEK. THE OLD BUTLER, WHO opened the champagne for her christening, told the hospital cook and the cook told Sergeant Sly and he told everyone else. So they all agree to give her a real " do." A surprise party planned and launched in secret. No one must tell her. She's coming to tea with Sister next Tuesday, for discussion as to which patients are fit to recuperate in her house. When the invalids regain their strength the Duchess receives many as her guests, for that little extra rest and comfort that means so much to people who have suffered.

Those who are already convalescing under her roof confer with less fortunate folk who are still in hospital nearby, and all are anxious to make a demonstration " come the day." It is the best possible excuse for festivities, both as a chance to amuse themselves and an occasion to express appreciation to their hostess.

Her grey stone house stands high above the bay. The junipers which flank it soften its severity and find an echo to their misty green in the waves far below., Peacocks sweep up and down the long terrace, their emerald necks bright as the jade pools that jewel the rocks and shore.

There is an air of great age and quietness about the place, which is heightened by the oldness of the retainers. The white-haired butler and his matching cook wife, who cater for the miscellaneous visitors with energy and skill. And the bent head gardener who has dug this ground for fifty years. For all his seventy summers he is active still, carrying vegetables to the hospital every day.

This is no decaying country house, its lifestream dammed and crippled by taxation and Victorian views, with shuttered, cob-webbed rooms falling into sickening uselessness, but a meeting-place for many whose homes have melted in the holocaust of war.

Here one floor is set aside for some Overseas men. They can come for leave, convalescence, Christmas, whenever they please and see English life from the inside instead of staying in the cold grandeur of London hotels which are all gold cupids, film stars and mock marble, and where no one ever shakes hands. Here they find something which cannot be purchased, riches of the right sort. Time, thought and money laid out with infinite pains to give others pleasure.

There is a restraint, dignity and kindly warmth about this great Cornish house with its wide-flung doors, where Dominion officers, English privates, old women from the London docks, hospital nurses, and even Sergeant Sly, who is an awkward fitter, feels welcomed and understood.

" It's because she's quality," says the hospital cook, who has been entertained there. " She knows her place; we knows ours and neither of us want it different. Give me the top people every time. The middle lot's no good. They want to be like aris-tocracy, but they can't behave right. It's knowing how to behave as makes people gentry."

I feel like that about Spike.

The war emergency hospital looks sad and grim after the Duchess's home. Once it was a golfing hotel, now, air-raid casualties of both sexes, and some dozen soldiers, are gathered there. The professional staff is lamentably small and overworked. Volun-tary helpers offer their services, which are thankfully accepted.

Here there is no glamour, no beauty. Only broken bodies, roughened hands, aching feet, black iron beds, forests of enamel bowls piled on trolleys, corridors reeking of disinfectant, cold bare floors and an atmosphere of forced brightness which deceives nobody.

One girl lost her arm when her flat was wrecked. Her face is terribly scarred. She was a street-walker, once sought after for her beauty. Now friendless. Alone. The old woman next to her is riddled with cancer. Her home, too, is a heap of rubble. Opposite a young Jewess lies with cascades of inky curls about her handsome face. Sly calls her Pearl of the Pacific. There is an Eastern air about her dark up-slanting eyes. She has made hats in Warsaw, Prague, Berlin. Her father has been in a German concentration camp for five years. At night she screams in her tortured sleep.

One of the nurses is Polish. All the sorrow of her land seems crystallised in the deep, dark eyes that have seen so much and tell so little. "I want to work—to forget," she says. Her voice is slow and sweet. Sister is tall, angular. A capable woman without warmth. Starchy in dress and manner. Does she ever relax or laugh with abandon?

The soldiers, and a few civilians, occupy a small separate wing. One is a gunner, with acute neuritis in his right arm. Some are "Gastrics." The airman has shrapnel wounds in his leg; two are A.R.P. wardens, wounded in recent raids.

How lonely these people must be, far from their homes and families. There are no distractions to cheer the deadly round of meals, washing, bedmaking. No relations with bunches of flowers, books and fruit drift into the ward at stated times to cheer the inmates with those little scraps of news and small gifts that shed sunlight upon the barren waste of illness.

It's a long walk to the hospital. Three miles of rough going, which diminishes the possibility of even stranger visitors. Lack of transport, rather than indifference, isolates the place. Pollyonites are warm-hearted, sympathetic, but most are busy, and few can tackle a six-mile walk in all.

Seats in buses can no longer be taken for granted. Those small certainties that made up the serenity of everyday life have vanished with nightgowns (all women sleep pyjama-ed in war), drawing pins, thick writing paper, fine silk stockings, quiet nights, and the means of seeing our friends.

Some of us know exactly what it feels like to be left behind because the bus is full; to struggle along with newspapers cascading from our arms in the teeth of an Atlantic gale. The fight for the few buses rivals the rush hour at Charing Cross. Everyone wants to get home for lunch or tea; there's an ebb and flow in the waiting crowd as the bus pulls up and school children dart like minnows between the sturdy old country folk who come in from the villages to shop.

Aimless drifting women with empty hands are told to pass right down the middle, adding to the discomfort and suffocation of all. Soldiers, who plod five and nine miles in from their camps stare, despairingly, at the choked vehicle that never stops for them. Mothers, carrying lusty babies, shift their burden from one arm to another, wondering when Cornwall will be itself again.

But if able-bodied folks feel lost, what is life like for these unfortunate people with aching bones and hearts whose sufferings are doubled because their homes have gone?

The very aspect of the hospital is forlorn, forbidding. There is sadness about the matted lawn, weedy drive and broken gate. Cabbages grow with healthy abandon in the round beds opposite the entrance. Little tin-topped wooden buildings cluster about the old one, hideous structures of mushroom growth. There is no shop, no cinema within walking distance of the hospital, so when a chance of this birthday merrymaking comes, both staff and patients determine to make the most of it.

Birthdays are festivals. This particular one is to be celebrated by a concert. Who will sing? Who will play? Cook has been heard to say that " that sergeant fellow can strum the piano like a nigger minstrel" and Miss Betty, " who is a reel Earl's daughter," played carols for their Christmas singsong. She works four days a week at the hospital, giving the women blanket baths, making their beds, doing every sort of heavy, dirty work with grace, intelligence and vigour. She hangs up her diamond wrist-watch on a nail above the sink, plunges her hand boldly into greasy water —and worse—— Not long ago she lived only for fox-hunting in Leicestershire.

"Perhaps she would bring her cinema," suggests Sly to Sister, who greets him with a brittle laugh. "The pictures are lovely, mostly China. Ever been there?"

"No." The answer is tart. She tries to keep away from Sly, but he draws her like a magnet.

"You go and find some greenery; we'll decorate the ward; have the piano at the far end with chairs grouped round. Will you see to that?"

He nods. Limps away. Firebrands like Sly must be kept busy. Anything to take him from that young scullery-maid—and she stumps away, never dreaming it's the Scottish cook with savings that lures him kitchenwards.

A hospital, like a ship, is a little world, where the paths of many meet, cross, and part, a segment of life, seen through a web of dreams. People pass through it, like a corridor, and play their tiny parts. Nurses, cooks, doctors, charwomen come and go. They run up and down and round about like ants, to and fro, unceasingly, cleaning, washing, sterilising, bandaging, cutting flesh open, sewing it up again. Knives and forks are crashed into the scullery sink; plates banged and chipped in the pantry; instruments and bowls for ever being boiled; mysterious bundles hurried away and burnt; there is no peace, no rest anywhere. The forthcoming concert increases the general activity. Floors, already immaculate, are scrubbed and polished harder than ever, and even personal preparations are made. Sister rolls up her lank locks into curlers at night in honour of the occasion, and a little warmth colours her chilly voice.

It is difficult to create a festive atmosphere without either balloons or a profusion of flowers.

"Wouldn't it be lovely if we could have balloons?" says old Mrs. Jenks, whose body is a mass of burns. No longer does she struggle to scrub herself piecemeal over the scullery sink. She is washed by Miss Betty, who smiles and says, "Now, up as far as the bandages, and down as far as the bandages." That takes the sting out of her pain.

"We'll try and find some balloons: I adore them, don't you?"

The girl's young, gay voice cheers them all. She toils away, twisting and twining great boughs of ivy about the ugly walls and doorways. Gradually the vault-like room loses its austerity.

Living green brings an atmosphere of hope and vitality with it. The bitter-sweet smell of ivy mingles with, and finally overcomes, the faint aroma of disinfectant that hangs, everlastingly, about these beds.

Those glossy leaves strike a different chord in every heart. The little Jewess stares at them, thinking how pretty they would look on a hat; the street-walker remembers the sun-flecked trees in a Sussex lane, long, long ago, before London attracted her; and one woman turns away from it all, thinking of her husband's birthday in a German prison camp.

"Look! Look! I've got a few balloons, not many, but better than nothing."

Miss Betty brings them in with triumph, hands them to Sly: "Here's a job for you, hope they won't break, they're old, probably."

One by one they go up, lovely dancing shapes of crimson, green, purple, red and gold, bright against the white ceiling. Mrs. Jenks watches the red one above her head. Red! Like the geraniums she grew on her London window-ledges. Her bed-jacket is red. The best of all colours. Gay, and somehow, defiant. Her hair has been washed. It fluffs out cleanly about her peaked face. Perhaps Nurse can find a bit of red ribbon to tie it up. Her thoughts turn to her husband. Where is he now. Has he got the birthday card she sent him of the little cottage with flowers round the porch? Is old Widow Sharp looking after him all right? Does she wash and mend and cook for him? A spasm of pain grips her. She closes her eyes: mind and body swamped with agony. The world slips away.

Meanwhile hospitality of another kind is being planned. Some friendly tradesman gives the soldier patients a lift into Pollyon, where they shop with open-handed enthusiasm, not to be baulked of their share in the celebrations. Cigarettes, beer, port, are carried home, not without peril, over the steep cliff path in the shortening summer twilight. Sixpences and shillings have been produced with astonishing prodigality. The kitchen staff have each con- tributed towards the drinks. Bottles and packages are smuggled away in readiness for the great day.

And when it dawns hospital discipline vanishes like smoke. Long shafts of gold fall across the beds, brighten the polished floor, and garlanded doorways. Tired, painful bodies stretch, and wake, glad to see the unaccustomed decorations about them.

Even the young doctor's professional manner melts after an innocent-looking glass of beer which the gastric corporal has strongly laced with brandy.

They all like the M.O.—he's a good fellow who understands them, but the chance to play pranks comes all too seldom these days, and it's fun to see how much a man can stand. It certainly takes effect. The doctor does not drop his stethoscope; nor does his speech thicken. But his eyes are opened. He speaks to Sister, now, as man to woman, noticing, for the first time, the lovely shape of her hands, her trim waist, long lashes. He forgets her uniform, her solid, unassailable status, so hardly won after long years of labour, and suddenly remembers that it's damned dull being a bachelor when you are young, stuck away in Cornwall.

For once Sister does not smell of disinfectant. A vague, flowery scent clings to her, lilac, honeysuckle, or lilies of the valley, something sweet and strange and lovely that frightens and disturbs him. She, too, feels different. Is it pity for the suffering people in her care or . . . just . . . beer? She doesn't know.

But Mrs. Jenks does. She understands, with the true knowledge of the very poor, how mellowing an occasional drink can be. One of the soldiers has smuggled in some whisky, decanted into an innocent-looking medicine bottle which instructs the reader to " Shake well. One tablespoonful to be taken thrice daily after meals." She has already drunk half and sees her little world through a blissful, clouded haze, where pain has, momentarily, died.

Nurse has tied a red ribbon in her hair to match the bunch of red balloons that billow above her head looking like blood-drops against the whitened walls. The doctor does not stare at her to-day in the puzzled way that frightens her. His face is neither grave nor pitying, but gay.

In the kitchen, main artery of every establishment, all is merriment. Here sound bodies eat their fill with the calm deliberation and intense enjoyment of those to whom sickness and suffering are happy strangers. But to-day it is drink, not food, that takes first place. Sly has bought a bottle of sherry. He has persuaded

Cook to drink two glasses and is now savouring her reactions with savage relish.

She has sandwiches to make for the tea-party this afternoon, buns to bake, a hundred jobs to get through, but she daren't rise from her chair.

Is she drunk? Surely not! Drunkenness is a vile, low state, associated with hiccupping, shaky legs, blurred speech. But she is floating—floating on a rosy cloud, and her legs don't shake. She simply hasn't got any. Where is she? Now she knows that a ticket to Utopia lurks in a wine bottle.

She sees nothing but Sly's mocking, handsome face. And she has the sense to sit still.

He has given her a calendar which caters for every possible eventuality, in addition to being a mine of information about Bank Holidays, new moons, and blackout times. In it she is told How to Make Your Will. How to Determine the Sex of Eggs. The plan of London Theatres and Tubes. Causes of Eczema. What to do in case of Fire. The Uses of Vegetables. There is also a Love Chart, with a wealth of detail about birth-dates, stars, colours and Marriage Partners.

" What star were you born under?"

She smiles and does not trust herself to speak.

" Mercury. That it?"

She nods.

" It says here all Mercury-born women beware of men with lame legs."

Poor soul. Sly drives her to the borders of lunacy. She is not young or handsome. She knows nothing of men and the capers they cut. But she has savings. Considerable savings, and she wants to marry Sly with all the force of her shut-up nature. Nothing on earth has ever mattered to her so much as this moody man with the quick tongue and strong red neck. He fell into her life, suddenly, like a stone into a deep, still pond. The way soldiers do.

His utter freedom of speech and manner alarms and fascinates her. He chats through the kitchen window, amused at her awkwardness, finding it, perhaps, a subtle change from the bold overtures of girls.

" What!" he would mock, " you shy of men, and soldiers

sitting about here all summer on the beach with no clothes on."

This staggered Cook so much that she fled into the scullery, slipped and crashed. Then he had hobbled in to pick her up, and for the first time, at thirty-five, she found herself in a man's arms. A terrifyingly sweet experience when it comes so late.

She had always been brought up to know that "men had a horrid side to them." Which is the "horrid side" of Sergeant Sly? Certainly not his chest, which she had leant against for one brief, ecstatic moment. A great tide of emotion had swept through her then, turning her legs and will to water. She had withdrawn from him, like a cornered animal, resolving never to be taken alive, yet passionately anxious to understand the strange thing that was flowering within her. Was he married? She could not tell. Dared not think. There were times when she hated him. But not to-day. To-morrow, when the tumult of work was done, she was going out with him, in her new flowery hat. And for all his banterings something told her that to-morrow would be a great day. Youth had passed her by. But she had possessions that were better than curly hair and pink cheeks. Money. Solid cash and the little bungalow that her father had left her, tucked away in one of Pollyon's coves.

Money is what matters most to the men and women of Sly's class. Yes, yes, he'd marry her all right, he told himself, but he must have a bit of fun first, pretending he wouldn't, play her like an awkward fish, now near, now far. But the end was never in doubt. You had to take your fun before marriage. There wasn't much afterwards. There had been none at all since Dunkirk, with this rotten leg that throbbed unendingly.

The party begins. The Duchess comes in and Sister greets her with a large bunch of pale pink carnations.

"From us all, with our best wishes and thanks. You do so much for us. We are very grateful."

"For me! Oh, how lovely, how kind of you! Who decorated the ward? It's charming, and balloons! Where did you get them?"

She goes from bed to bed, smiling, talking in her easy way. Others come in behind her—all her household staff and visitors, the Minister, Mrs. Blunt, Mrs. Treloon, the Jolly family, a bunch of soldiers from the canteen whose lusty voices will swell the community singing. Typed songs are handed round to patients and visitors: Sergeant Sly begins to play.

There are three soloists—a Canadian officer, a nurse and a wounded London Air Raid Warden, who perform in turn. This has a loosening effect upon the general company, who are shy to join community singing before each other. Those who habitually bellow in their baths are now dumb. But Sly knows exactly how to manage them. Perhaps he has been a professional. He runs through one song after another, all the old favourites, and the new, marching songs, sentimental songs, gay songs, sad songs until the audience begin to shout their choices. If they are slow to start they are far slower to stop. Not until all are hoarse and hot is a halt called for Miss Betty to erect her cinema.

Then there is a movement in the background. Someone is coming forward.

" Flanagan's going to sing!"

" Well, if he wants to, let him."

" But he can't! You see."

" Maloney's Moll, let's 'ave Maloney's Moll." His Irish voice cannot go down on paper. Sly has vanished. Who can act as accompanist?

" Come on now, don't you all know it?"

There is a horrid hush followed by whispers of " Lady K—— is here, she'll help him out."

Miss Betty's mother, a tall woman with long white hands goes to the piano and whisks over the pages of the British Song Book, praying that the vocalist may change his mind and ask for the Londonderry Air or John Peel or anything that she played to her children long ago.

" But it is not here," she pleads apologetically.

" Never mind, Madam, we'll sing, and you follow along."

Off he starts, entirely out of tune, beating time with his hands, others chip in with more enthusiasm than harmony and Lady K—— flounders manfully, to pick up the air, first wrong, then right. She can play Chopin very well, but finds it difficult to catch the rhythm of this. Finally she masters it completely and is given a great round of applause for her good-natured determination.

In the lull which follows Lady K—— glances anxiously at the

bed patients, who are propped up in the stiff attitudes from which some cannot move without help. She whispers to a nurse, who shakes her head.

"No, no, not a bit necessary . . . we train them . . . only every four hours. They are quite comfortable."

The one-armed girl is very pale. Mrs. Jenks laughs and claps, but there are moments when the whiplash of pain flicks across her face. The Jewess, with her long glossy curls, rounded cheeks, black-fringed eyes looks like an exotic flower against her white pillows.

They don't ask for anything. They don't complain, so it is taken for granted that they are "quite comfortable."

And now curtains are drawn and pictures spring to life on the silvery screen.

Then tea. Trolley tables are pushed in with fat brown teapots and piles of dainty sandwiches altogether different from the customary food. Miss Betty cut most of them and carried them up the hill in a tin wrapped about with wet cloths. All the Duchess's guests and the hospital inmates have contributed something. And there are small fresh scones. So Cook has come back from the Elysian fields.

Beer, cider, cigarettes are set out upon a side table. The recently recovered wait upon those who are still recumbent, and hover about the Duchess, drinking her health.

"Happy birthday!"—"Good luck!"

"May your new year bring peace with it."

It is plain to see that she is deeply touched. There is a buzz of conversation. "Feel funny to be out of bed?"

"Gettin' used to your crutches?"

"Doing fine; two more weeks and it's home for me. You here much longer?" Then the pathetic answer. "Don't know." Behind the plucky off-hand words is the frantic feeling of having nowhere to go. Some will pack their few belongings cheerfully, glad to be gone. Others wait with piteous anxiety wondering if brother William or sister Fanny will offer to take them in. But no letter comes and the distance to passing-out day shortens with dismaying speed. Mrs. Jenks worries over that.

At last it is all over. The beer has been drunk. Teapots grow cold. The ivy about the doorways look a little tired. Hand-shaking begins. The Duchess goes to every bed, the gift of flowers in her arms.

"It's been wonderfully kind of you. Thank you so much: a day I shall always remember."

The ward is cleared, straightened, crockery carried off, washed, put away. The daily routine, momentarily discarded, is picked up again.

Temperatures are taken; charts filled in. Helpers walk home and night comes down. Night that is not night, but rather a jewelled silver clasp linking sunset to dawn.

Sister takes off her cap and starchy dress, scrutinises her fine features with misgiving. She has often wondered what part of her would "go" first. She knows now. The eyelids. Funny things human bodies, lumps of flesh and blood and bone, instruments of the most intense joy and indescribable agony, working, loving, living, for ever seeking their counterpart.

She has begun to fight the grimmest of women's many battles, a rearguard action against oncoming age, when all resources must be gathered and flung to check the inexorable foe. Not for reasons of vanity, but from sheer, stark necessity. She has no reinforcements, no reserves but her own courage and unflagging will to keep going. No weapons except a blunted sword. Will it always be like this? . . . Summer after summer, alone?

Sergeant Sly steps out of his trousers wishing he had given Cook a powder-puff instead of a calendar. Her face was shining this afternoon. Not like that girl in Bombay with magnolia skin. Never mind. He has felt happier to-day and wonders why. Cook went to bed early, with her calendar under her pillow, her new hat laid ready for the morrow. One by one the lights die. Shadows thicken in the passages, footfalls echo away into silence. There is only a glimmer of light in the women's ward, just enough for Mrs. Jenks to watch the red balloon above her bed. Then that, too, is dimmed. The hospital sleeps.

The tragic day comes when hospital patients must be discharged. Soldiers rejoin their units, after brief leave. But others have literally nowhere to go. Mrs. Jenks is one. Her Stepney home is wrecked; she is childless. Her husband sleeps in Widow Sharp's front room. The bed is grimy; the street foul. No place for a dying woman. They'd always had window-boxes full of red geraniums. Red. Like that balloon Miss Betty hung over her head. The colour of blood.

She has something worse than burns. Underneath her raw, scorched flesh is a huge, vigorous growth, spreading . . . spreading. Nothing can stop it. She will soon be utterly destroyed. But her bed is wanted. She must go.

So the Duchess drives down to fetch her, slowly, over the rough white road, through blinding sunshine. Sister, knowing how short her time is, comes out to say good-bye. Mrs. Jenks is driven to the great house that is full of dim portraits, deep carpets, long velvet curtains and furniture that is old and bloomy, like sherry in the sun.

The invalid is helped into the hall where massed scarlet flowers answer scarlet candles in slender silver candelabra, and Chippendale chairs have seats of red brocade, worn and dulled by age to a beautiful dimness. Huge logs are laid across the stone fire-place ready for winter nights. Where will she be when they burst into crimson flames?

Not here.

She climbs slowly, painfully upstairs into a little room with rose-bud hangings; an easy-chair; green carpet. Her eyes swim, seeing the place where her husband lives. She turns to her hostess with an eager, grateful smile.

" This is lovely—lovely. Can you really keep me for a fortnight? Then I shall be strong enough to go back. It's a long time since I saw my husband."

She has been robbed of much, but now she sits in a house like those she has seen on the films and a " titled lady" with diamond rings waits upon her with a friendly smile.

What is the future of the little street-walker? She has learnt to dress herself, curl her glorious flaxen hair, with the remaining hand. She, too, must go.

" My friend has a flower shop in London. She has asked me to work in her office. I can write with my left hand. I'd never be happy outside London."

And Sly? What can he do but play the piano—and who wants that? Nobody. The bitter knowledge has now come to him that his leg will never be sound again. Another three weeks' treatment —and then—the cook. The hospital cook, for ever and always, in that little cottage down on the cream-coloured sands. She never questions him; she's kind, gentle, stupid. Perhaps her sanity will help him to regain his own; he likes to watch her doing simple, fundamental things; making tea, washing dishes, peeling potatoes, sweeping the kitchen.

If only she were beautiful as well. His thirst for beauty is unquenchable. But gradually the crawling horrors that infest his mind are weakening. He still remembers what he has seen, felt. Every night the pictures of it rise before him, but they are less vivid. There are times when he forgets them completely.

Why? He doesn't know yet.

The sheer loveliness of Pollyon is seeping into his scarred soul, healing, comforting, beautifying its tortured waste, driving out the shadows that are so slow to die. Every city, county, town, village has its own character and atmosphere. Instantly felt. Always remembered. Pollyon has caught, and kept, the spirit of lovely and abiding things.

All the colours in creation are gathered here. The aquamarine and amber of smiling days when the sands are almost white, and the cliffs are carpeted with coral flowers. In a far field the redness of poppies bleeds among the ripening corn.

Colour lurks in every fold and twist and turn of the rocks, from palest amethyst to wine-dark purple, from sapphire to indigo, from living gold to grey. And not all the jewels in the world could equal the iridescent splendour of the peacock-tinted sea.

Huge caves fringe the pearly shore, and in hot weather their yawning mouths show every shade of green, blue and black, caverns of coolness faintly streaked with celadon shadows as the sun falls on them, dark as violet velvet in the twilight when only sea-gulls flutter about their deserted depths. If the rainbow ends anywhere it is surely here.

Chapter X

THE CANTEEN

Pay day. Friday afternoon. The narrow stone passageway, scrubbed now twice weekly, is thronged with men, chattering, laughing, whistling, gloriously alive. And yet shadows of departture deepen in this gaunt house; the air is full of farewells. A facet of life that has been caught, held, and brilliantly illumined is now slipping into the limbo of past things.

Hay harvest is over. Flaming poppies have lived their short life and the upland where they bloomed is no longer red, but gold with ripened corn. Not for another year will lilac and honeysuckle blow about the gardens and fields of Pollyon.

The Royal West Hamptonshire regiment go next week and the Ploughshires will be moving soon. The Duchess has already gone, taking Daisy with her. She has been restless for a long time, this job was far, far too small for her, and now she has a big important one that will leave no time to think when work is done.

Isobel, too, has vanished; she is driving an ambulance and the little cream-and-scarlet shop has been taken over by a white-haired woman who is too old for so much. The rooms where Freddy Fenshaw spent his last and all his leaves with Isobel are now full of strangers.

" We're off on Monday!"

" This 'ull be the last time we come in!"

" Anuther lot is due next week."

The news passes quickly from mouth to mouth. Alf is very excited at the prospect of a move. He hates Cornwall, and though he doesn't know if he is going to Singapore, Colchester or the Middle East he doesn't care. The mere fact of getting out of Pollyon is a tonic to him. His effervescent Cockey mentality thrives on excitement, even if it only means marching to the station with a kitbag.

" We're off to fight the Germans!"

" When we choose they'll get it."

The Ploughshire Colonel comes in. His eyes that looked so old are young again. He smiles happily.

" Is the canteen going well?"

" Yes, thank you; we shall miss your men."

" They've enjoyed coming here."

A girl is with him. A girl like a colt; all legs. Very good legs.

" This is my wife."

So she did say Yes.

And we are going back to Norney Rough to tackle life from yet another angle. It seems that the design for living must be revised with every passing year.

Nurse has " joined herself up in the Air Force" as Sue expresses it. Nursery life must soon come to an end. " Alas! . . . that youth's sweet-scented manuscript should close!" The high-sided plates of babyhood, so charmingly enlivened with Goosey Gander's rollicking and imprudent experiences, are now outgrown, and mugs, painted with all the flowers of spring, must be discarded. Small fingers will grapple with family china (and how lamentably dull it will seem after the Miss Muffet variety), little legs will dangle from large old chairs, and little blobs of porridge will fall upon the dining-room table that is like wallflower velvet.

Alice writes: " the vegetables is lovely and the chimneys have been swept it is very hard to get a sweep as I know you ordered him weeks ago. The Colonel says 'Well Alice we shall all be very sorry to lose you it will be hard work making those large bombs' and I said I felt I ought to and he said of course and knew you would too."

Perhaps some day, somewhere, as the throaty crooners declare, we may find Alice's counterpart in the new world that we must all build together.

But in future we may not be able to afford an " Alice." One maid costs a £100 yearly including wages, food, insurance and laundry. That's a lot. But if we had no maid we shouldn't save a £100 a year. Far from it, because then I should have no time to grow vegetables, make, wash, iron, mend for the family, and transport them to school by bus or bicycle.

And now there are to be hens as well crowing for attention. But Chanticleer will wake us in the late summer dawns. There is no need to wind him up or put him on ten minutes or hide him under a pillow like the kitchen alarm clock. He senses that the night has gone, long, long before dawn flushes the waiting sky, and from his iridescent flung-back throat the news is born— Morning!!

" Seems funny without her."

Spike jerks a thumb towards the corner where Daisy's cage once stood, and his eyes come to rest upon the place there the Duchess always worked.

" And the lady; I shall miss her. Nice lady, she was."

" You'll be going before long. Are you glad?"

" Glad? No. Sorry. Very sorry. I likes Cornwall. It's kinder quiet: country, like wot I've been used to. I'd rather stay here."

He counts the money out, slowly, carefully.

" Two Cornish pasties, please. It's pay day to-day."

A smile deepens in his blue eyes.

" Wish they'd let us help cart the harvest; just the weather for it."

His father will be lumbering over the Oxfordshire fields now, his mind in the future, as a countryman's always must be. Will he have to plough this long upward slope again this autumn—and next? Sow the winter wheat, and harvest it for yet another season almost unaided? He is tired—tired, and help is hard to come by.

Perhaps his son will be back next year—out of the Army—the war finished. But it's now he longs for lusty arms, and the strength to work daylong through gruelling heat.

Ginger Scot leans against the counter. " The West Hampton-shires are reel upset at leavin'. So are we. Everyone has been verra kind."

What a lot these men have taught us. They are clean, tidy, cheerful under all circumstances. The very smallest things give them pleasure; a walk by the sea; cups of tea; singing round the piano; a game of darts. Small pay and an unknown future never dims their gaiety.

" I 'opes we go to London." That's Alf.

" Maybe you will. They want a sentry outside the Palace while the Guards are fightin'."

Guffaws and jokes fly round. The men are lively with that sense of expectation which comes when uncertainty lies ahead. Alf may have disliked Cornwall, but it has done him good. Like castor oil. His spots have gone; and he seems to have grown all over. That may be in part, at least, from bathing.

He still talks. " Parliament's full of Germans, full of Germans it is. But Churchill 'ull clear 'em out. He'll wake us all up and Germany too, sure 'e will."

Nobody is listening but that doesn't stop him.

" Russia and the Abyssinians 'ull get their own back; you see. Christmas will see the finish of it."

Unlike his comrades he has no capacity for stillness or silence. He can't sit and drink his tea, peacefully, or look at a paper for more than a second. Little Alf is as fussy and fidgety and talkative as an old lady in a cathedral town. He has a passion for the cinema.

" Seen the newsreel this week? You go and see the King. Marvellous 'e is, marvellous."

An occasional visit to the cinema has become a happy event. Films now supply all the riches of life unseen elsewhere. They provide us with blazing lights pouring through open windows; bare shoulders; dinner-jackets; orchids and the spectacle of people with no larger troubles than the uncertainties of love-making. How cheering to see men in faultless clothes smoking cigars with an air of unhurried richness; to watch exquisitely groomed women drifting about satin-hung bedrooms.

A body that is not well cared for quickly becomes revolting. Rough hair, rough hands are hideous and must not be permitted. And though half-inch talons are wholly unsuited to practical working lives the sight of them is a reminder that even the most useful fingers can be beautiful. We must hold fast to beauty amid the monstrosities of war which thicken on every side.

Tanks, tin hats, sandbags, terrifying figures wearing decontamination suits, gas masks and women's bare legs. The last are almost the worst of all because they were there before the war and they will be there after when all the other trappings of combat have happily disappeared. Stockings will return, but we shall never forget that Mrs. B.'s shins are a network of moles. Slim tanned calves can be beautiful in the right setting of heat, bare to the thighs when topped by a charming face, graceful figure. But shopping streets on dull cold days are now thronged with pallid, hairy and bowed understandings. Rough red heels, insteps that are a mass of thick bluish veins and nightmarish knees. It is a revelation to see how many women are built, like dachshunds, with Queen Anne legs. But like all parts of female anatomy women's legs are tough, enduring. They are willingly exposed to scorching heat, and chilly damp winds, thus saving coupons for the more vital family protection in winter. Daddy's chest, many little cold, ever-growing toes and the fingers of wage-earning boys who bicycle to work in winter winds, must, somehow, be covered warmly. So the sight of all these mottled legs is but a reminder of the picture that lies behind them.

It seems wickedly luxurious to relax in a one-and-tenpenny velvet chair for two hours, instead of hurrying through the day's work. An air of guilt pervades any form of recreation, however brief it may be.

But it's wonderful to see glimpses of British history that will last for ever. The Home Guard on duty at Buckingham Palace; what a queer twist of fate has brought them there. The *Bismarck* heeling over; a grandmother of seventy who dragged four children out of a tottering, blazing house.

And then comes the picture of men walking through streets fringed with shattered ruins.

Whispers pass from one to another, like breezes across a cornfield. " The King! The King!" Yes, it is he. Not the remote

figure in a golden coach but a man in uniform, walking like everyone else. Only a few years ago the populace thronged about his
carriage cheering themselves hoarse, to see their monarch going
to be crowned.

Now he comes to them in their agony of slow death, pain and
grief, the cruellest torture that men and women and children have
ever been called upon to bear. And again they surge about him,
not with wild demonstrations of excitement, but in a quieter way
which is infinitely more impressive.

"The King! The King! God bless him! Long Live the
King!"

No visible bodyguard protects him; no fat, shapeless bullies,
bristling with revolvers, who strut and shout as Germans do.
There is no one to clear the way. Neither pomp nor ceremony
attend him and yet there is an extraordinary dignity about his
figure.

The National Anthem swells from a thousand throats as the
people follow him along the smashed and smoking streets, the
ruins of happy homes where men and women have been killed.

Years ago when London crowds called for him outside Buckingham Palace on Coronation night they cheered him for what he
represented. Now they love him for himself—his courage,
resolution and understanding.

We are grateful to the wordy Alf for his cinema suggestion.
He does talk sense sometimes.

Monday morning and the Royal West Hamptonshire Regiment
swings through Pollyon outward bound. That's all they know,
or say. The sun, best of all benedictions, shines on them and the
little town wears her most exquisite dress of azure, cream and gold
in honour of their departure. Blue sky, white-tipped waves,
stone-coloured houses gilded by the warm light. And where the
sea caresses the dark rocks the water is shadowed with pansy-petal
velvet. That is the picture they take with them.

Here they come! Left. Right. Left. Right. The throb of
their feet, heartbeats of the Empire, resound about the street.
They pass the canteen with its small Union Jack. Their symbol.
Our spur.

Traffic turns aside before the curving column. The red laundry
van bringing clean sheets to the Crescent Hotel, pulls into the gutter

of the narrow way; the postman, wheeling his bicycle up the steep hill moves on to the pavement, and a large green bus stops in a side turning as the living barrier pours past.

No horn is blown; street life automatically comes to a standstill before this phalanx.

When will these men see England again?

Pollyon people, who open their arms to strangers, now gather to wave farewell.

Cornishmen, for all their friendliness, are at heart remote, not easily touched. Then why do they stand in the streets this morning to wish the soldier God speed? They can visualise and understand the hazards that rule his life because the same streak of uncertainty runs through their own existence. They serve the earth and sea, cruel, capricious masters that take bitter toll. There is a curious link between people who are quiet with that stolid sort of strength which grows from endured, and surmounted, hardship.

The old fisherman says, " Good luck go with you," as the troops stream by. Both land and water have claimed his sons. One was drowned steering the lifeboat in monstrous waves; Cornish sailors are shining figures in the history of the seas. Another died beside his gun firing, firing, unsupported, alone, until the end. His sons live again in the hot pulsating bodies that file so steadily before his ageing eyes. The same brave blood, the same stout hearts, and the same traditions are here in all their magnificence.

That's why he lingers to see them march away.

Miss Blossom and Jenny, in whom youth has long since died, wave with enthusiasm. Old Jenny, in her full print skirt and crown of white hair, looks like Mrs. Gilpin running out of a Caldecot drawing. Mr. Friske stares at the serried ranks with regret and pride. These soldiers have nothing, but everything he wanted most is theirs. An outdoor life. Freedom that goes with it, not freedom from work, not freedom to do as they please, but freedom from all the hideous trappings of a cooped-up life. Like a rat in a trap; that's all he'd ever been. Starved of all that mattered most.

The sailor's " bride" wearing only her overall, wedding-ring and sandals, waves and throws kisses to the boys with gay abandon. Sailors were more her line, but there is an irresistible attraction about the " military." The booking clerk, ignoring impatient passengers rapping their money for tickets, leaves his pigeon-hole and joins the thickening crowd upon the platform. This is a bit of life and he means to see it. Ah! to be one of them. He forgets his trim villa, careful wife, laboriously accumulated savings, all the hedged-in dullness of his life. Barriers everywhere. Laurel bushes between him and his neighbours. " Booking Clerk" written on his door. " Porter" pasted on the next. Tiny walled-in cubicles where lives are spent in barren loneliness.

But it's one thing to see soldiers marching down a sunlit street, another to share their hardships. The sight of them brings a great sweep-up of emotion, an urge to honour them, do them service, no matter how small. But we can only stand and give them a passing cheer, as we do when His Majesty goes by. We cannot tell the King's men the pride, the love, the terror that mingles in our hearts to see them.

The Minister is here. His flame-like personality draws all about him. Long after Cornwall is forgotten this man will live in their memories: a star blazing in overwhelming darkness.

The two bandy-legged porters, valiant veterans who have filled the gaps made by younger men, await the coming of " the military" calmly, hands in pockets. " The military" make their own plans; you can't say anything to them; they order you about. That saves a lot of trouble.

" Thank goodness, soldiers don't want nuthin' carried for 'em." It's no fun carting other people's baggage about at seventy-two.

And there is no ticket taking. The Government pays. Troops don't fumble for their fare or ask when the train gets in or where they change. They just come—and go—in perfect order, and although they have so much to carry nothing is ever lost or left behind. A miracle of organisation.

The train comes in backwards, as always. It slides to rest, slowly, slowly against the buffers, gently as a balloon loosed from a child's hand, and the great gay engine faces away from the station —outward bound. It is gloriously alive; smoke pours from the fat funnel, sparks and flames leap and glow inside its portly black body. The truck of coal hitched on behind gives an air of un-rationed richness to the whole turn-out.

The driver, a cheerful, dusty-faced fellow leans out to catch a glimpse of the goings-on. He generally takes a few old people, babies, pigs, hens from this station to the junction beyond. This is quite a change. He lights a cigarette, leans comfortably against a pile of inky fuel and chats readily.

" Yes, twenty-nine years I have driven this train; to and fro three times every day. Never been late yet. Looks like I shall be this morning."

He hardly could be behind time since he has two hours in which to do a run that takes only half that time. But Harry doesn't know soldiers. Many hundred men can entrain quicker than the dozen old countrywomen who peer into their purses forty times to see if their tickets are there and if the booking-clerk gave the right change. They know the train would never go without them. When Mrs. Polwellin failed to appear one Friday scouts were sent out to look for her. She had travelled in this train, to draw her pension, for longer than anyone could remember and a panting porter returned to tell the driver " Not to wait, she died last night."

Strangers to Pollyon, asking what time the next train is due, have been startled to be told " Should be eleven-forty, but it all depends on wot time 'Arry starts."

Harry starts when he is ready—not before.

The men surge over the platform. A human tide. Mrs. Treloon and Mrs. Blunt carry great baskets of home-made dainties. Cornish pasties, savoury sandwiches, rock cakes. With characteristic sense they wait until the men are free of their heavy gear and have found seats. Then they walk up and down proffering their gifts to outstretched hands. Even Mrs. Treloon, a victim to her own tribal laws, is touched to-day.

" We've had a good time here."—" Thank you very much."

Hand-shaking, munching, exchanges of pleasantries fill the last minutes and all the partings of the past live again in this one.

Soldiers. Soldiers. The sight and the sound and meaning of them never leaves us. Even when they have marched away we can hear their laughter, their voices and their feet.

Then the train comes to life and face-lined windows move slowly away. A regiment looks its last upon a Cornish town.

" Good-bye." " Good luck." The same old words. There are no better new ones.

They have gone. Well, we still have the Ploughshires for a little longer, and after that the toy train will come for us.

Chapter XI

THE RAID

The children are on the beach searching for the semi-precious stones that are as colourful as their rich-sounding names. Banded agate, chalcedony, amethyst, crystal and jasper. The stone cutter can make an ashtray of agate that looks like a captured cloud streaked with imprisoned sunshine, or a crystal paperweight of iceberg coolness. Even in their rough natural state the pebbles have a beauty of their own.

Hot, panting, industrious, Sally and Sue run up with these lovely simple products of the shore.

"For Dad! Look! A present for Dad!"

Surf and sands are alive with schoolgirls bathing. Their bright swim-suits look gay as nasturtiums in a cottage garden. The shadow of a Dornier flies high above the cream-coloured Cornish town. It passes away and is forgotten.

But in the short summer nights that follow others come again and again.

War-time days are strange, but nights are infinitely more so. Once all the business of living ended abruptly at a given hour, from nine to midnight, according to taste and inclination. Then we slipped thankfully away into that twilight place between life and death " where all things are forgotten" and emerged from it at morning time new men and women strengthened; resolved.

Now the barrier between night and day has been swept away. The switch of life is not turned off at will. Mind and body are watchful, vigilant, taut, ever ready for what those droning planes may bring. It is extraordinary to know death is so close at hand. We all want to live now that there is a chance that we shall not. Having started a job we like to see the end of it. What will Europe be like in ten years? Will George really make a good soldier? And will someone with tumbled curls and wondering eyes find happiness among all our broken gods? But no matter how long our sojourn we shall never see the finished pattern into which our tiny threads are woven, sometimes clumsily, in plain dull colours without beauty, sometimes well done with strands of gold.

These long wakeful nights have their advantages. Working hours are stretched ever longer. Bodies and brains perish utterly if coddled but revive when lashed, and war jobs, sewing, knitting are done far into the night between midnight and morning almost as a matter of course. Minds range into regions undreamed-of when sleep was an unthanked-for blessing.

I have spent an imaginary hundred pounds on Norney Rough a thousand times over, with intense pleasure when eyes and brains were too tired for active use. A white bedroom with touches of faded red and old, old furniture. The smoking-room " done up" so that anyone might be glad to have tea in it. And we will have new curtains. Very grand ones in the children's bathroom of North Sea green. That was the name which the svelte young man gave to the material long, long ago before a siren had sounded in London. " Green, Madam? Yes, we have a wide range, this North Sea green is lovely." It was. With tiny white ripples, as of breaking foam flickering across it. Thin, tenuous stuff, silky as skin. Another year and the nursery bathroom won't have a boat in it, or rubber toys, or very short dressing-gowns hanging on the door. Bathrooms, like their users, must grow up. What happy moments were spent in that tiled cubicle, watching tiny baby limbs promoted from the comforting smallness of a rubber bath into the glossy porcelain depths of adult adventure.

Then the great day when little hands could take out the plug, turn on the taps, and, last phase of all, " wash and dry myself." That stage will soon be reached. New curtains won't simply be a purchase, they will be a milestone on the widening road.

The cot has been empty for a long time, yet we still cling to this family treasure with its halo of happy memories. All the cousins and nephews and nieces have peered through those bars for thirty years. Its successive occupants are soldiers, nurses, ambulance drivers, schoolgirls now, but a little pink and white tenant may soon bring back the miracle of life and love to the cosy cushions which have pillowed so many downy heads.

Then a close crash wakes Sue as the windows rattle.

" I'm warver cold. Can I come in your bed?" She feels warm enough and her eyes close instantly again. Sally sleeps on.

The general loss of sleep bothers people more than the lack of meat and sugar. The butcher leaves all the wrong rations at the Crescent Hotel sometimes and apologises, explaining that he is so overcome with drowsiness that he can scarcely tackle the two and three men's work that now falls to his lot.

Twice weekly he patrols the cliffs as a Home Guard, often in wild soaking weather. And he must be a meat purveyor again by 7.30 a.m., hauling, chopping and then delivering carcases. He runs the business alone. And he is not young.

Sometimes we all get eight hours of unbroken slumber. Sometimes the planes go over and over for a short time, then we are left in peace.

Pollyon lost many hours of sleep when planes passed overhead, but Pollyon did not get out of bed until the first bomb fell.

Raid technique has been rapidly perfected since then. As the siren goes, Father leaves his well-earned rest, puts on his tin hat and sallies forth. Mother gathers the children about her in their selected place of so-called safety—pulling the curtains even closer —thankful for the smallest activities to still the agony in her heart. Books and chalks keep little fingers happily employed. The eldest boy wrestles with his carpentry unmindful of danger. A spade, shovel and box of sand stand in the corner of the little room. A First Aid Box and A.R.P. leaflets lie on a shelf.

Long sickening whistles reverberate and whine above the little house. Mother fills the kettle, takes up her knitting. One hour passes, then two, three, four. She puts the children to bed in the narrow passage under the stairs, dozes on the sofa fitfully herself, planning the holiday that they will have when the war is over. Perhaps their sister in London will invite them for a week and she will be able to buy a navy crêpe-de-chine dress with white flowers on it, and white shoes with high heels. High heels spell leisure, as do the inch-long nails of her favourite film star. She has almost forgotten what leisure means.

Then her husband stumbles in, filthy, exhausted. His face is blackened; his hands scratched and bleeding. But he is alive. That is enough.

" A fire: two cottages. No one hurt but all the furniture's gone." It might so well have been their own.

After the war. After the war. To stand above two sleeping faces knowing that death from the skies no longer shadows them; to open the paper and not see " Killed on Active Service." To lie down and sleep in the sure knowledge that no British man or woman remains in a German prison; to make up the fire with a clear conscience because no British soldier is numbed with cold in Hell's own country; to feel that, once again, British sailors face the sea that holds " no enemy but winter and rough weather."

That will be peace indeed, no matter if our purses are empty, our homes let or sold to swell incomes that grow ever smaller. And we shan't have to eat carrots or potatoes twice daily any more —unless we want to.

Then we shall be sole, and not part, owners of our garments; there will be no need to ring up Mildred and say, " If not already booked, may I have your blue outfit for Jane's wedding? Would you like my best shoes and stockings for the week-end?"

Borders now full of lettuces will live again in red, white and blue that will have an added glory. Scarlet poppies, Sweet Sultan, and veronica, most heavenly of blues, will melt into each other, with brilliant abandon, while tobacco plants billow against the yew hedge where over a thousand carefully counted tomatoes are gathered in these war years. Fat glossy balls that Sally and Sue pick each evening for their supper, as soft and warm and healthy as their own plump cheeks.

"Tomatoes, give them plenty of tomatoes," advise white-coated dentists and black-coated doctors.

We can't give them more; they'd burst. Not the tomatoes. The children, to whom the dangers of inflation are unknown. Perhaps that is why the family is free from scurvy, rickets and that depressing state known as "general debility."

Problems of every kind will face us. The shortage of hitherto commonplace things may give rise to new situations. Cars, bicycles, houses will be hard to come by. But having shared underclothes, coats, bacon rashers and sugar lumps with our friends and relations, no flicker of surprise will betray us if strangers arrive, cheque-book in hand, with such overtures as "I will give you two, three, or four thousand for this house; three pounds for your bicycle; a hundred and fifty for your car." What a temptation when the bank balance is scarcely showing! It might save trouble then to have thermometers on our front doors—as we now have in the High Streets of Godalming and Pollyon registering the War Savings—so that all comers could see that a mere £3 11s. 9½d. reposes in our bonny, bonny bank.

Just think of it, this fat man with, obviously, the millions of Israel behind him, is willing to give three thousand pounds for Norney Rough. He wants to sit down at my desk and write out those figures on a bit of paper, hand it to Nick and then say: "Now your house is mine." What's the good of three thousand pounds if you haven't got a home? None whatever. We wouldn't let him have it for four, nor five. It is too precious. If a buyer must be found we will choose one. Who'd give a dog to somebody who didn't care for it? Who'd sell a house to a purchaser who only wanted four walls and a roof? He wouldn't know the difference between daisies and buttercups; he'd keep the rooms at 70° from October till April, never notice that magical day when winter dies and spring is born. Would he ever see the dawn yellowing behind the larches on cold, sweet October mornings; would he cut the lavender on hot August days, and dry it, thinly laid out in the hall window, so that all the house was drenched with its fragrance? Would he see the pimpernels, the speedwell, the fox-gloves about his feet as he walked through the wood where Sally once saw a fairy? No.

" We are sorry. Norney Rough is not for sale."

Night-time is sweetened by the thoughts that come and go when bombers hover above our children, and mental corridors are swept clear of all but fundamental things. The fragrance of yesterday. The hope of to-morrow.

Every night now shoes and warm jerseys are put by the children's bedside. Ought they to sleep always in the shelter which is neither warm nor dry? It's difficult to decide.

As the sirens wail Sally is woken and bundled into the clothes which lie ready. Then little Sue is rolled up in a blanket. Their tossed hair and rounded pink cheeks have never seemed so dear. We hurry down to the refuge room.

How heavy a sleeping child is. Terror, born of helplessness, rises in me, as I gather up her warm weight. " . . . he that hath no sword." The silvery night air is rent with the steady hum of our fighters mustering to meet the enemy. They wheel, gather, and sweep upward toward the broken throb that is now sickeningly familiar.

Doors open all along the corridors, giving up their dead. Old ladies with white pigtails, and sensible dressing-gowns. The bride, in foamy satiny frills, befeathered mules, with her drowsy sailor husband to whom sleep is the rarest and most precious luxury. A trim woman in slacks and jersey. Men, with bare, stringy necks, rumpled hair. Some dream-dazed children.

" Dumerdumerdum. Dum-er-dum-dum." Miss Blossom beats out the rallying call to refuge on the dinner-gong with the vigour and thoroughness of an African chieftain. Her frock is unbuttoned; curls and complexion in disarray. A little bag containing her " valuables" dangles from her wrist. What are they? None can tell. Something that she loves dearly since the reticule never leaves her sight. My " valuables" are at Norney Rough. The ring that Nick gave me in Hong Kong when Val and " Jackie" stood there wishing us good luck. Well, we have had it. A letter from Mr. H. E. Bates, and the dining-room table. All highly prized for widely varying reasons. Treasures beyond price.

The semi-underground garage is eventually reached by about forty of us. Mattresses that look inviting, but are really damp, chairs, tables, disused furniture and oddments of china are scattered about. The stone floor strikes cold and cheerless; one faint electric bulb illumines the gaunt building. But it has mere slots of windows —is sturdily built of stone and concrete and therefore is safer, perhaps, than our roof-top bedrooms. It is certainly quieter, and sleep means everything to little ones.

Sue is laid on a sofa, snugly enfolded, her tiny, sun-kissed hands clasped together. Someone has brought a wireless and turns on music from a London restaurant. The sudden, harsh noise does not wake her. She sleeps on and on, beyond the realm of sound. A two-months-old baby whimpers. The father is an airman. He has never seen his child.

Dull thuds and a spatter of gunfire can be heard, then utter silence save for baby breathing, followed by splintering crashes and the steady drone of engines. We stare at each other for comfort, finding distraction in unexpected places. The fact that Mr. Friske's bare chest is matted with black hair, while his head is silver grey: that Mrs. Friske's side teeth are missing, and Miss Blossom is unrecognisable and infinitely prettier without make-up, holds attention, if only for a moment.

Mr. Friske, cheerful as ever, in spite of getting no rent from the row of abandoned East Coast houses that belong to him, slaps his doleful neighbour on the back remarking: " Courage, mon ami." They subside, squashily, upon a damp mattress likely to render the sitters home-made casualties.

" Courage isn't for sale here," is the shrewd retort. The speaker's eyes are on a stupid woman, chattering hysterically.

"That's a near one. Where do they take the dead people, leave them in the streets?"

" A doctor tells me that the only cure for hysteria is a slap on the face. If that does no good smack the other cheek, much harder."

Mr. Friske speaks with deliberation to no one in particular. The babbling ceases.

In the corner a man sits writing on the edge of a wooden wash-stand. He is completely clothed, even to collar and tie. Wholly absorbed, he pushes the paper upwards, forgetful of the yawning hole usually occupied by a basin. Letters and pen fall through. He laughs good-humouredly.

" Never written on a washstand before."

He looks about, picks up a bit of cardboard, blows the dust off, covers the crater with it and continues writing.

Some women knit for the children who lie so trustingly beside them. Others work at pullovers of Air Force blue, khaki socks, seamen's stockings for next winter.

Next winter . . .

A terrific explosion, then gunfire, louder, nearer. Sally, wide-eyed and wondering, smiles at kind Mr. Friske, who pulls comic grimaces at precisely the right moment. She is not afraid. How do I know? Impossible to say, but I do. Fear is something that she has never seen or felt. Yet she must be bewildered. What is passing in her mind? It is difficult to explain enough and not too much. Will fear be born in her to-night, the frightful spectre that is so hard to kill? And if it is, will this horror haunt her always? Is our third generation to be wrecked in mind, if not in body?

Sue gives a little sigh, stretches, curls up again. A motor-bicycle rips up the street. Two cars flash by. Minutes drag on leaden feet. Somewhere a clock strikes one. It grows colder. Sally sleeps against my arm, warm fingers entwined with mine.

Planes drone backwards and forwards. Backwards and for-wards, searching, relentlessly, for a target, over the town, towards the camp, back again. Ours, or theirs? Difficult to tell.

This one is close. It roars overhead and we brace ourselves for what may come. There is a long whistling wail as the bombs are loosed. I pull a cushion over Sue's small, calm face and fling a rug about Sally's head instinctively. The very earth is rent; the quivering floor heaves like a tarpaulin in a gale. Something seems to burst in our ears and throats and hearts and then, silence, except for the fading hum of the departing plane and a ripple of relief that passes over us all.

Half-past one. Sirens scream again. Back to bed. Sleeping children are carried upstairs by flickering torchlight. The cars go by again, slower now, with their tragic burdens.

Spike is dead. Murdered as he lay sleeping.

" Two poached eggs and tea, please."

" Packet cigarettes, thank you."

"No sugar: fourpence, that right?"

Hands perform their mechanical tasks; bodies run to and fro, but hearts are ice-cold and eyes blinded. Alf is speaking.

"'E came right down to a few hundred feet, with his engine shut off, the sentry says. Ginger Scot's in hospital. He caught it properly."

The heroes of Dunkirk. Ginger's voice comes back. "We did our best but we hadn't got the guns."

"The fighters went after 'im, shot 'im down in flames over the sea."

"Coupla doughnuts, please."

The fat, sugary ones that were bought for Spike. He would have been here to-day, Friday. Pay day. Happiest evening of the soldier's week. He generally tramped in the five or six miles over the cliff path, twisting giddily high above the Atlantic wastes.

"I like a walk," he would say, slowly, wiping his face. "We get a lift back sometimes."

His words were few—yet they are remembered.

"Cornwall . . . is kinder quiet . . . I'd like to stay here. . . ."

His clothes were rough, uncomfortable. His pay small. In winter, snow and rain and wind tore and lashed his body. He was often wet for days together, raw, chilblained feet aching in stiff, clumsy boots. How hot he had been in France. Blinded by blood and sweat and dirt under the merciless sun, with no brightness anywhere except the gleam of British bayonets and the spirit behind them. Spike was a stranger always to comfort, luxury, indulgence. Germans killed him in his sleep.

The stainless day is quiet with the ripe warmth of late summer.

"Lovely for bathing!" We gather up the children's towels and cross the road as a lorry rumbles by.

It is full of wreaths.

"How pretty, look at the flowers! Is it a wedding?" Little Sue dances across the pavement.

A few hours later there is a sound of drums, not triumphant, reverberating, the loved music of marching men, but muffled, the saddest sound in all the world. It grows louder—louder. And then the cortège comes into view up the winding street.

The coffins are made everlastingly brilliant by the British flag that enfolds them. Never have the colours looked lovelier. Not even the massed flowers can dim their beauty or significance. Black-coated mourners follow behind. Is Spike's mother among them, or is she in her Oxfordshire cottage where she gave him birth, stricken now, as then, with agony?

He will not be alone on the long dark journey. Others of a great and gallant company have gone with him, and, perhaps, the faint remembrance of fresh, sugary doughnuts, strong, sweet tea (stronger and sweeter than we had any right to make it), and English roses on the table. Perhaps, too, a misty memory of one who honoured him above all telling.

Men stand bareheaded in the road and women wipe their eyes as the long procession passes. Girls, in cheap finery bought to attract these men who are now dead, huddle together in awestruck misery, white-faced, bewildered. One is shaken by terrible sobs.

The Crescent Hotel dining-room is full of people lunching. Old Jenny and the little housemaid, hopelessly outnumbered, are struggling valiantly with the waiting.

"Potatoes, can we have the potatoes?" demands Mrs. Friske. She lost at bridge last night and is still irritated by the hollow triumph of her opponents.

"Yes, Madam, just coming." The girl turns to the serving-table, stretches for the dish, and then her hands fall, lifelessly, to her sides. She stands transfixed to see the sight outside.

"Can we have the potatoes?"

But the waitress, blinded with tears, stumbles into the pantry. Jenny, reared under the iron hand of discipline, snatches and proffers the belated vegetables, but now even Mrs. Friske is smitten with silence. Her husband is standing. Others follow his example, and Jenny, quiet and dignified, remains holding the cold, forgotten potatoes in a trembling hand.

Good-bye, Spike. . . . "So he passed over and all the trumpets sounded for him on the other side."

Day fades to its shining end and the long green Atlantic twilight enwraps the little town. The toy train puffs across the fields. It brought us all here. Spike, Ginger Scot, Sergeant Sly, and hundreds of children. Two regiments. Isobel and her soldier who found, and lost, their dreams.

It will take some of us away, but a few will sleep here always. As the albescent light of a rising moon falls upon the face of the waters the star-strewn sky is racked with the roar of machinery. The planes pass over. Sometimes there is silence, an unearthly period of stillness and expectancy between the deep voices of the far-off guns.

At last "All Clear" shrills across the paling darkness. Then an answer rings out from the tumbled ruins of the camp. Reveille, with its promise of resurrection. The night has gone. Here comes another day.